JOHANNA'S WORLD

JOHANNA'S WORLD

Ø·M·ANDRESEN

TRANSLATED BY JOHAN BONNEVIE

HarperCollins*Publishers (New Zealand) Limited*

The author and publishers wish to thank the following individuals and organisations for providing copyright material or assisting with the preparation of this book.

Descendants of Johanna and Christian Christiansen: Niel Andersen, Ormond 'King' Andersen, Betty Brownlie, Ena Dawn Christiansen, Alex McCallum, Alison Morgan, Joyce Otterson and Eileen Williams; Norsewood Pioneer Museum; National Archives of New Zealand; Family History Section, New Zealand and Pacific Room, Palmerston North City Library; the following newspapers (1871-1936), *Daily Telegraph*, Napier, *Evening Post*, Wellington, *Feilding Star*, *Hawke's Bay Herald*, *Manawatu Times*, *Waipawa Mail* and the *Wanganui Chronicle*.

First published 2000
HarperCollins*Publishers (New Zealand) Limited*
P.O. Box 1, Auckland

Copyright © Øystein Molstad Andresen 2000

Øystein Molstad Andresen asserts the moral right to be identified as the author of this work.

All rights reserved. No part of this publication may be reproduced, stored in a retrieval system or transmitted in any form or by any means, electronic, mechanical, photocopying, recording or otherwise, without the prior written permission of the publishers.

ISBN 1 86950 370 8

Set in New Baskerville and Optima
Designed and typeset by Chris O'Brien/Pages LP
Printed by Griffin Press, South Australia on 80gsm Econoprint

Contents

Acknowledgements

I spent eighteen months during 1996 and 1997 in New Zealand, researching this book, and during this time I lived in Palmerston North and Norsewood – where I was quickly renamed Stan!

The original version of this book, published in Norwegian, is named *Uredd ferd mot ukjent land* (Fearless journey to an unknown land). It was first published in August 1999 by Genesis Forlag, Oslo.

I would like to point out to the reader that aspects of the family's life, how they spoke and acted, may differ slightly from their real lives. Similarly, some people who feature in the book, especially those portrayed as close acquaintances of the family, may be composite characters drawn from the life experiences of a range of people associated with the time and the places referred to in the story. However, the story of the migration from Norway to New Zealand, along with the general history of Norway and Southern Hawke's Bay during the period covered in the book, is based on primary, secondary and oral history sources, including extensive use of the newspapers of the day.

While I have written six other books, I consider the migration story portrayed in *Johanna's World* my most important work so far. I feel that by now I must know more about the migration of Norwegians to New Zealand in the latter part of the nineteenth century than any other living Norwegian! This is thanks to the efforts of historians Hans Marius Trøseid and Bjorn Neskvern in Norway and Val Burr, MA (Hons.) in New Zealand, who also prepared the manuscript. I also greatly appreciate the help of Johan Bonnevie, who translated the book into English, ably assisted by Sigga Bonnevie, Eileen Williams and Alison Morgan, who assisted with proofreading, and secretary and archivist Maria Dau Andreson.

Øystein Molstad Andresen
Hamar, Norway, 2000

Introduction

Emigration: an historical overview

In the year of our Lord 1873, a small group of people, fourteen in all, left the parish of Grue in southeast Norway. They were bound for New Zealand, but no one knew for sure where this country was. Only that it was far away.

This book deals with these people and a handful more. All had links with Pasotorpet, a tenant farmlet, deep in the forest and so isolated that after their departure it was never occupied again. The farmlet, close to the Nord-Odal border, is situated on the western slopes of Pasoberget (Paso Hill), which is 472 metres above sea level. Altitude alone makes farming marginal. However, the view across Meitsjøen (Lake Meit) is beautiful.

Pasotorpet belonged to Skara, a farm in Solør, which at the time was divided into seven farmlets, three in Skara East and four in Skara West. All seven had a stake in Pasotorpet, due to the land-ownership practices of the time. In 1873, the three Skara East farms had separate owners, but in the late 1800s, they became the property of a single owner. Until recently, the present owner of Skara East also owned Pasotorpet. However, subdivision of the forest has now placed it under Bjerke farm.

Many people left the impoverished parishes of Solør, Nes and Odalen before the family from Pasotorpet. Migration registers record that between the years 1870 and 1875, 165 people left this district en route for New Zealand. Most likely, the figure should be higher as not all of those who left had their names entered in the official register.

The emigration chain to New Zealand from this part of Norway reached its peak in 1872, with (officially) fifty-six people – along with several hundred other Norwegians – leaving Christiania (Oslo) aboard SS *Høvding*. The following year, at least another thirty-five passengers from the same district again sailed for New Zealand aboard *Høvding*. Of these, the largest family group was the family from Pasotorpet.

At least 312 persons from the Solør-Odalen district headed overseas in 1873. However, clearly New Zealand was not the preferred choice for most of them. In fact, some 267 headed along the well-beaten path toward America. Migration from Norway (and Europe in general) to America declined sharply around this time, due to an economic depression in the United States. Norwegian emigration statistics for 1870 indicate that 14,838 people left Norway. This equates to 8.55 people in every 1000 of Norway's mean population. Throughout the brief period where New Zealand assisted Norwegian emigrants and other Northern Europeans (1870-1876), Norway's emigration rate dropped to 7.4 people per 1000 in 1871, 7.9 in 1872, 5.86 in 1873, 2.58 in 1874, and 2.24 in 1875.

The United States' economy recovered as the decade continued and this influenced New Zealand's own decline into economic depression in the late 1870s and early 1880s. Many of New Zealand's struggling new immigrants suffered badly as a result, as vital sources of Government-sponsored employment soon dried up.

Migration from Europe to the United States quickly recovered as that country's economy improved. It even drew some of those who had been assisted to come to New Zealand. They now seized the chance to escape New Zealand's depression, and to head for what may always have been their preferred destination.

The passenger list, signed on 12 August 1873 by Captain C. Nordby and the ship's doctor P. Mogstad, was not compiled with care. Research shows slipshod work. Names were misspelt, and children were not necessarily matched with their parents, although older teenagers would have been listed – and accommodated – separately from their parents. Furthermore, as with the previous *Høvding* voyage, addresses were often excluded or simply marked as 'from the interior'. To make matters worse, the passenger list shows sixty-five people from the Solør-Odalen

Norwegian Places of Origin	Migration to America	Migration to Australia	Migration to New Zealand
Solør	5		
Vålor	36		
Åsnes	25		
Hof	2		
Grue	36		14
Brandval	44		(from Pasotorpet/Skara
Vinger	39		1
Kongsvinger	9		(Arne, the shoemaker)
Eidskog	33		6
Sør-Odal	8	1	15
Nord-Odal	30	3	5
Total	**267**	**4**	**41**

Numbers of people recorded in the Norwegian Emigration Registers as migrating to various overseas destinations from the Solør-Odalen district in 1873. That year, some 10,352 people (or 5.86 per 1000 of mean population) were recorded as having emigrated from Norway, although Norwegian migration was declining steadily at the time. (Sources: Research in the emigration registers by Hans Marius Trøseid, and Val Burr, in *Mosquitoes & Sawdust*, pages 5-6)

district, instead of the aforementioned thirty-five, making the home regions of another thirty people uncertain.

One may well suspect that Captain Nordby considered poverty-stricken passengers to be goods for delivery, rather than human beings needing care. What we look upon today as basic human rights was far from his way of thinking.

Why did they leave?

The 1815 census lists 3450 souls then living in the Sør-Odal (South Valley) district, which is some 100 km from Oslo (Christiania) as the crow flies. Fifty years later, the population had reached 7118. Furthermore, in the adjoining Nord-Odal (North Valley) district, where Pasotorpet is located, the population increased over the same period from 1600 people (a rather 'round' figure suggesting guesswork) to 4310. However, no farmable land remained to be wrested from the forest. Tenant farmers on their meagre holdings faced real hardship, and starvation was a constant threat. The 1865 census shows that the large family at Pasotorpet possessed: one horse, three cows, three sheep, ten goats, one-sixteenth barrel of rye, one barrel of barley, one-quarter barrel of oats and three barrels of potatoes. A starvation diet indeed!

Emigration to America at this time was a real godsend – provided one had the money to purchase a ticket.

Over the next ten years, Sør-Odal's population reduced from 7118 to 6834, a nett loss of 284 people. Meanwhile Nord-Odal's population decreased from 4310 to 4166, a nett loss of 144 people. Still, the poorest of the poor had no money for tickets. For them, emigration only became possible when the seemingly generous New Zealand Government offered them 'free passage and almost free land'. At least, these were the conditions as would-be emigrants understood them.

These were the expansive days of Julius Vogel's overly optimistic Immigration and Public Works scheme. This scheme assisted migration to New Zealand in order to permit quick land clearance, and the building of light railways and roading networks. The New Zealand Government wanted people with experience in forestry work. No wonder the agent they sent to Norway turned his eyes to the Odalen district. The poverty-stricken tenant farmers occupying this heavily forested area were well-used to forestry.

Who were they?

Let us take a closer look at the family living at Pasotorpet in 1873. Head of the family was Johan Johannesen Paso (43), who was married to his second cousin, Randi Finnsdatter (44). Eight of the couple's ten children were living, and seven were still living at home. These were: Fredrik (20), Johanna (17), Bertea (15), Karoline (13), Randine (10), Karen (7) and little Julius, who was only 6 months.

Five others joined the party that left Pasotorpet in late July 1873. These included the couple's oldest daughter, Berte Maria (23), her husband Ole Olsen (28), who was a farm worker from Kuggerud, and their children: Anne (7) and Arne (18 months). The fifth was Christian Christiansen (23), who was from

Steinbekken, another tenant farm under Skara Farm. He would in due course become Johanna's husband.

By the time the family emigrated, four generations – spread over more than a century – had struggled at Pasotorpet. Each generation had endured hardship and hunger, a fate that seemed unlikely to be shaken off on this farm. Like so many others of his own generation, Johan Johannesen Paso sought relief from this endless drudgery. He dreamed of freedom and the chance to be in charge of his own future. Doubtless, his forebears had shared his thoughts – he was the one who received the chance.

Others from the district who boarded SS *Høvding* in August 1873 were:

Sør-Odal Parish:
Karen (Johan's younger sister), her husband Ole Christoffersen and their four children, Christoffer (16), Marthea (9), Julie (6) and Ole (2). Also Jakab Isakson (30), his wife Karen Larsdatter (31) and their children Ole (7) and Carl (5).

Nord-Odal Parish:
Johannes Johannesen (25), his Swedish-born wife, Martha Olofsdotter (30), and their son Oscar (6 months). Also, the widow, Karen Pedersdatter (38) and her two children Kari Tostensdatter (8) and Tosten Tostensen (6).

Eidskog Parish:
Hans Larsen (31), his wife Anne Olsdatter (43), and their children Karen Gulbrandsdatter (13), Oline (4) and Lina (1).

Vinger Parish:
The shoemaker, Arne Christiansen (36).

Where did they come from?

The Christian name Johan occurs repeatedly in the Pasotorpet family. The 1686 census shows that Johan Simensen Paso, born in Sweden of Finnish parents, had settled at Finnskogen, Norway. In about 1770, his grandson, Johan Johannesen Paso, settled at Pasotorpet and cleared the land there. Since the farmer at Skara owned the vast forest that included this property, Pasotorpet became a tenant farm under Skara.

Over time, the real family history became lost – or rather, it became somewhat 'improved upon'. The new 'attractive' version claimed the family came from the French aristocracy, when an indiscretion at the French Court made it necessary for the family's illustrious forebears to flee to the deep, dark forests of Odalen, where they would be safe. What perhaps began as someone's bedtime story went on to enhance the family's self-image, even in New Zealand. Other emigrant families also improved upon the stories of their impoverished origins.

SS *Høvding*, of Tønsberg

The three-masted, full-rigged barque, SS *Høvding* (Chieftain) made two voyages to New Zealand carrying emigrants. The first voyage, with 483 passengers, left Christiania on 30 May 1872 under the command of Captain C. B. Berg, of Tønsberg. It arrived at Napier on 15 September 1872. In 1873, the ship repeated the journey, albeit with a new captain. Captain Berg had been killed in an accident on the return voyage from New Zealand, as the ship loaded guano in Peru. On this second voyage, the ship carried 369 mostly Norwegian men, women and children, including the Pasotorpet party.

Høvding was built at Tønsberg, to the design of Jacob Jensen (born 1820 at Stavern), and was launched in 1867. A. B. Bull, owner of the Tønsberg shipyard, was also the ship's first owner when it entered service. The timber used in its construction came from Forenbu, near Oslo, which until October 1998 was the site of Norway's international airport.

Considered very fast, at one time *Høvding* held the record for crossing the Atlantic. That run, carrying timber, took place between Miranich, Canada and Liverpool, England.

In 1909, the elderly ship became a lighter based at the timber town of Fredrikstad, southeast of Oslo. Some publications describing *Høvding*'s eventual fate, claim Japanese bombs sank the ship in Darwin Harbour during World War Two. This seems highly unlikely and probably involves another ship with the same name.

Further reading

The following publications were used by the author in researching the story of the family from Pasotorpet.

Andersen, A.L., *Norsewood: the centennial story* (1972, reprinted Stoke, Nelson, 1997).

Appendices to the Journals of the House of Representatives (AJHR), 1892.

Burr, Val A., *Mosquitoes & Sawdust: A history of Scandinavians in early Palmerston North & surrounding districts* (Palmerston North, 1995).

Davidson, J.W., *The Scandinavians in New Zealand* (A thesis for BA Honours in History, Victoria University College, Wellington, 1936).

Norsewood Pioneer Museum Committee, *Norsewood, New Zealand* (Norsewood, 1985)

Norsewood School Jubilee Committee, *75th Jubilee, Norsewood School 1874-1949* (Dannevirke, 1949).

Olsen, Johanna E., *Fragrant Reminiscences* (family publication, circa 1980).

Olsen, Johanna E., *Reflections of Yesteryear: A dedication and tribute to Mother* (Dannevirke, 1985).

Thomsen, Brian, Percy Ridge & Charles Vaughan, *Norsewood School Centennial, 1974* (Norsewood School Centennial Committee, 1974).

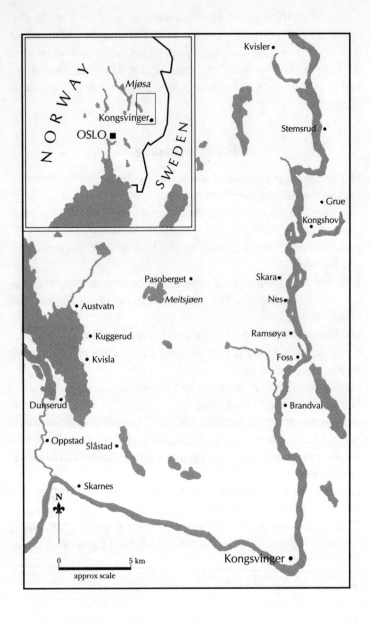

'Thank God, the worst is over' said Old Paso.
They had reached Kuggerud farm at Odalen.

Part I

Towards the Unknown

1 The die is cast

PASOTORPET. The word has a melancholy sound. A sad piece of music, like the never-ending sighing of fir trees. Here people toiled for generations but left little to show for their labours. Pasotorpet still exists, even though the forest has attempted to conceal it. I should confess that I could not have found it without Hans Marius Trøseid and Bjørn Neskvern, who are both local historians as well as pathfinders. Their knowledge, of both past and present, was amazing.

It feels strange to seek out building sites in the wilderness. Could this depression in the ground have been the barn? And this one the cow byre perhaps?

Traces of the Paso folk remain. Great mounds of moss-covered stones lie between the trees. Not one or two heaps, but over a dozen remain to confirm that once the land really was cleared. Here were paddocks and tilled fields. Potatoes and barley grew. The Paso cottage still stands, but no longer firmly. One corner is sinking. Heavy rough timber, grey with age, contains networks of cracks and veins that resemble old worn hands. Stinging nettles surround the cottage.

How many blueberries there are. Big, shiny and deep blue,

growing in the shade of the trees, as far as the eye can see. It is mid-July. They are all ripe and there is no one to pick them.

In mid-July a century and a quarter ago, a young girl aged 17 had walked here, barefoot, picking blueberries. What were Johanna's thoughts, as she prepared to leave for a strange and unknown world?

I sit on the nearest moss-covered stone heap, close my eyes, and my thoughts are sharpened. Blueberries and mossy stones, grey timber walls and tall trees. All have something to say. Will they tell me the story of Johanna who once lived here?

Johanna sat down when she reached the clearing east of Pasotorpet. From this knoll, she could enjoy a wonderful view of the area far beyond the river Glåmma. This was the last time she would run barefoot through the forest. She needed to fix this memory in her mind forever, and take it with her to her new land. She had been here many times before. Even as a child, she had played and dreamed here. The gnawing hunger pains were forgotten.

She wished to take only happy memories with her; of summer, songs and games, discoveries, warm smells and dappled sunlight on the forest floor. Her happiest moments had been spent here. Running barefoot like the wind and later returning to Mama Randi, filled with excitement, her mouth stained blue from eating blueberries. In these places, she met goblins and dwarfs and fairies – all a little shy and melting away in the forest. All true. She saw them all. Even trolls, bigger than trees, had appeared – and disappeared.

She wanted this sun-drenched summer afternoon all to herself, in mid-July 1873. From where she sat, she could see the hills far to the east. They rose lazily one behind the other and shimmered in the haze, the last almost as pale as the sky itself.

What would the future be like? She had no idea. She only knew that her parents' decision followed the arrival of Uncle Christoffer's letter last spring:

Catch the Høvding *when she sails next July or August. I can assure you it would be a wise decision. The journey is virtually free and on arrival, you can have 40 acres of good land very cheaply. Here you are your own master and don't have to slave away under a wealthy farmer. I have just bought very good land for £1 per acre from the government. They will also lend us £14 to buy tools and provisions. In addition, they offer us work five days a week, eight o'clock in the morning to five in the evening with one hour off for lunch. And we get five shillings a day. The soil is good and needs no manure. But we cannot harvest anything yet, and much work lies ahead as the forest has to be cleared away. The trees are very big, some up to 56 feet around the base. You ought to come. Back to Norway? Oh no, not any of us.*

The letter bore the postal stamp: Norsewood December 1, 1872, and was signed Christoffer Finnsen, Mama Randi's brother. The Finnsen family had signed the emigration register and set out for the unknown the previous year.

Reckless, people had said. The family had left Christiania on 30 May aboard *Høvding* and had arrived in Napier on 15 September 1872. Uncle Christoffer wrote the letter just over two months after his arrival in Norsewood.

Johan had been beside himself with excitement when Johanna read the letter aloud. The daughter made the best sense of what was written and could make the words flow. She had been to school, unlike her parents, and did not have to struggle with every single word.

'There lies our future, Randi.'

Johanna could still see her father's face. Mouth half open, eyes wide open and with an expression of disbelief, until he fully understood Christoffer's letter. Then he had stretched across the table, taken both Randi's hands and whispered with the greatest of seriousness: 'There lies our future, Randi.'

But Randi was not convinced. At least not at first. She

could not believe her brother was so able with pen and paper. When he was confirmed in the Lutheran Church at the age of fifteen, he could hardly write his name. Now, here was a beautifully written letter. Full of big words, and with phrases that were difficult to understand. Quite unbelievable.

Her skepticism subsided as Johan's enthusiasm gradually won her over. His instant conversion came with a great sense of relief. He shook with laughter when Johanna read the letter for the third time.

'Not a slave under a wealthy farmer. Oh, that was well put.' The planning started at that very moment.

Johanna feared the thought of leaving everything she knew and held dear. In spite of Christoffer's optimism and encouragement, a nagging doubt remained. There must be dangers lurking there too, only different dangers. Some things didn't quite ring true. Her uncle was a man of few words, simple words, yet now he could express himself most eloquently. Believe it or not, some Swedish words had slipped into the letter as well. Still, her doubts – and Randi's – were quickly dispelled, as both her father and her secret sweetheart, Christian, took up the same slogan: That's where our future lies. That settled matters for the blushing Johanna.

Just this summer she had felt the stingings of young womanhood, the prickling sensation, the yearning and need to have someone dear. Christian Christiansen, 23 years old, a farmhand at Skara, was the cause. He saw that their future was far away, beyond all oceans. With Christian, she could travel to the other side of the world. He was strong, yet so gentle. He understood everything. His face looked honest. And when he looked at her with his clear blue eyes, and spoke softly and thoughtfully, she felt wonderfully empty and warm – and safe.

Long ago, Christian had decided what he wanted from life, or rather, what he did not want. He had no desire to go through life with his nose to the grindstone, someone else's grindstone, as his own father had done, just as his father's father had done, and the father before that, and that again.

No, away, away. Away to the Promised Land, to America and freedom. He admired those who had left for America. The ones who had struggled to save and had eventually scraped together enough money for a ticket. He felt the pull to the unknown that they, the earlier emigrants, must have known.

Johanna smiled to herself. Her thoughts wandered back to that evening in early June. Christian had called in at Pasotorpet – supposedly to catch a fish or two in Meitsjøen. He had then announced he had bought a ticket, not to America, but to Canada because it was cheaper. Teasingly he asked if she would care to follow one day, but, oh, he was in for a shock.

Inside the cottage sat both her parents, deep in conversation about an unknown land called Ny Seland. They showed him the letter from the family who had emigrated the previous year.

'That's where our future lies,' said Johan Johannesen Paso, for about the fiftieth time. His voice had become a little louder each time his confidence had increased. Christian, once seated, heard more of this land, apparently flowing with milk and honey – and which eagerly awaited new immigrants.

'We'll all go there, all of us. Whoever . . . Whoever will, can take over Pasotorpet. Can take over this heap of stones! Welcome to it all, stones and more stones!' Then he turned to Christian, calming down a little, and looked him full in the face. 'If you want Johanna, you had better come too.'

He had said it! Oh, how she had blushed, and then hidden her face in her hands. Her father had tried to marry her off – but Christian had not proposed at all, that time in June. He'd only asked if she would come to Canada some time, perhaps.

Poor Christian had looked very uncomfortable. It was all too much for him, and too sudden. Still, when he caught

Johanna's eye he had smiled. And she had smiled back; a shy, little smile, careful not to appear brazen. But behind the smile was something she could not hide. She feared losing him. If they went in different directions now, they would certainly never see each other again.

Christian, dear kind Christian, had then solved it all. 'I think I'll sell that ticket to Canada.'

So it turned out. The other farm worker at Skara, Adolf Knutsen, also wanted to emigrate, but had been unable to scrape up enough money for a ticket to either America or Canada. Now, suddenly, here was a ticket going cheaply – and Adolf was overjoyed.

There lies our future. Johanna had been lost in thought. It had been lovely to think back to that evening in early June.

The row of blue hills beyond the river Glåmma were still there, and were just a shade darker. She had never been as far as Glåmma, only as far as Nes and Grue – and to Kuggerud and Oppstad on the other side. That was far enough on foot. Now, though, she was to travel beyond all oceans, to a land called Ny Seland. Did the water from Glåmma reach as far as that? She knew all water, from streams and river, eventually ended up in the sea. Still, would it stop there, by the coast, or would it flow on to the other side of the world?

There were trees in Ny Seland. Huge trees too, Uncle Christoffer had said, but were they fir, spruce and pine trees, tall and trim with red trunks? And did they sigh and whisper overhead, without the wind telling them to do so? Would there be juniper and heather there too? And lingonberries and blueberries and the warm smell of mosses? She breathed deeply. A small voice inside her said: 'Hold onto it all. Hold onto the pale distant hills and the red pines, the heather and the blueberries and the good summer smells of the mosses and the forest floor.'

Johanna pulled a big fir cone from the clutches of reindeer lichen and studied it carefully. Then, with practice from her childhood, she picked a twig, broke four pieces off and poked them into the long cone. Two at each end.

Lo and behold, there was Daisy, her favourite cow, once more. She had always played with cones, like other children of the poor. The smaller cones became sheep or goats. The larger ones, from fir trees, were Daisy, Rosie and Molly – Mama's three precious cows. Still, Randi had done very little milking in recent years. The four youngest girls claimed much of her time – and now, of course, there was Julius, only 6 months old. From the age of 5, Johanna had accompanied her mother to the cow byre. It was a warm place with a range of smells, but it could be a little frightening all the same. The cows' teats, though limp, seemed to lead lives of their own.

'Moisten, squeeze, pull, squeeze, pull,' said Mama, but it had taken a long time before the milk flowed freely into the wooden bucket. When Karen was born, seven years earlier, Johanna took over most of the work with the cows, although Bertea and Karoline helped with cleaning up. Every morning, after milking, they swept out the byre to keep the floor dry and clean. It was often strewn with juniper needles by the time the cows returned. Daisy, Rosie and Molly appeared to like the fresh smell of juniper, as they stood there contentedly chewing their cud.

The goats also needed milking. There were ten of them, but only six were then in milk. To begin with, they were a real nuisance. Johanna was too small to stand over them and hold them between her knees, but she was too big to milk them while she was seated. They were such restless creatures as well. They were always trying to get into the cottage, as they knew where to find the salt.

Oh yes, inside – not the scullery where the salt was kept – but the real inside, the big room, which held such strong feelings of security and family togetherness. This room contained two long benches, always shiny, polished by over a century of Paso bottoms. Between them stood the table, just one thick, huge slab of pine, which was almost white with the effects of age, water, lye and sandstone. Such a beautiful table. Twelve round depressions, six on each side, were still visible on its surface. It was from these depressions that earlier generations of Paso children had eaten their barley porridge.

A very old, dignified-looking triangular cupboard stood in one corner. Had it come from France? Johanna wondered. Then there was the big bed for the children, attached to the wall on one side, with sturdy legs on the other. That wonderful spinning wheel stood in the far corner. Many years ago, the goats had knocked it over and damaged it severely. Papa had taken everything apart, remade some bits and restored others. Now the spinning wheel sang more sweetly than ever, so Randi said. And Johan liked being praised by his wife.

Papa was undoubtedly very clever with his hands. He had made the two baskets next to the spinning wheel. These were knee high, fairly narrow. They were made from the bark of silver birch trees, over a light frame of willow saplings. They were beautiful and glowed in the candlelight. One basket contained the raw wool, just as it came off the sheep's back. The other held carded wool, rows of smooth tufts, placed crosswise, this way and that. Papa did most of the carding. He had gentle hands when these were needed.

Johan was also very handy with his axe, and was known for his skills even beyond Odalen parish. Was there anyone who could make wagon wheels to match his? They seemed stronger than anyone else's and lasted longer. Several farmers had asked for help from Pasotorpet when they needed the very best wheels. They knew the woodwork, as well as the heavy metal band from the local smithy, would be the best shillings could buy.

Johanna's mind returned to the spinning wheel. She could see her mother in the evening, pulling the spinning wheel out from the corner and finding the place where it could be properly balanced on the uneven floor. She would start spinning and the old wheel would come alive and begin humming with pleasure. The tufts of wool would become long, even threads between sensitive fingers. Her shadow would dance rhythmically on the wall, keeping in step with the music of the wheel. It was easy to fall asleep then, under the sheepskin blanket. That music was, surely, the sweetest cradlesong. Bless that spinning wheel. It was an essential part of Pasotorpet, perhaps even the heart itself. It provided the clothes for the whole family. They must never part with it.

Johanna too, could spin. She mastered the art at the age of 12 and now had countless balls of wool to her credit. Spinning was one thing. Knitting was another. She did not know when she learned to knit, perhaps she had known all her life. She made almost all her own clothes, other than some handed down by Berte Maria, or by the Lutheran pastor's wife at Grue.

Her favourite part of working with wool was giving it colour, to dye it with plants from Our Lord's own garden. Again, the pastor's wife had been so helpful, and so good to her. Four years ago, during the spring of Johanna's confirmation year, these lessons had begun. The pastor, of course, taught the spiritual lessons and made sure the proper catechism would stay with the young people for life. Lessons on the Ten Commandments, set questions and answers, had to be learned by heart.

Somehow, the fortnightly lessons always started early. The pastor's wife encouraged the girls to meet in her kitchen and there they assisted her to dye wool. Rhubarb leaves and walnut skins, acorns and juniper bark, and other things from the pastor's large garden, all played roles in the process. Wood ash and a little salt were added to make the colours stick – and then . . . The excitement was great when the wool came out of the steaming vats. No one ever knew what the colour would be. Oak leaves, from last autumn, would normally give a soft yellow colour, but if God wanted otherwise, it could have a distinct greenish hue. Blue was impossible to achieve. With all their experiments that happy spring, they never managed anything that looked even a little bluish.

The pastor's kind wife sent the girls home with samples of coloured wool. She also made them write notes on how each colour was achieved and encouraged them to experiment further at home. Occasionally the girls also went home with a loaf of bread. Not all the girls, but the ones who lived furthest away. Spring was a difficult time, and tenant farmers were always the first to run out of flour.

Johanna continued to experiment at home, using twigs, bark and leaves. Flowers, no matter how beautiful, never gave any colour away and she soon knew not to use them. Reindeer moss and lichen slowly became her favourites. Lichen hanging in spruce trees like old beards, or better still, lichen scraped off big stones. Pasotorpet had a great selection of these, although most stones had not been out of the earth long enough to gather lichen. Johanna wondered why greyish white lichen gave a soft pink colour. As the water with nature's gifts boiled in the big iron pot, she would plunge the wool in – only for a moment – then fish it all out with her stick.

For days afterwards, silver birches around Pasotorpet supported wool from their lower branches. Long streamers of wool – sandy-coloured, soft, light or dark brown, shades of yellow, or simply pinkish. She found knitting the different colours together very satisfying. Patterns would be devised, and here she was her own teacher. Bands of yellow or dark brown would appear on sandy-coloured jerseys. Karen had a horse on her jersey, while Bertea had a troll on hers. The little girls were delighted. Imagination always worked within Johanna. Her fingers itched with creativity.

Randi was a little puzzled about all this. Patterns and decorations were neither part of her work, nor part of her nature. Clothes kept the cold out and warmth in. However, she was secretly proud of her daughter, and of her special gifts.

'They must have come from your father,' Randi said. 'Or from your grandfather perhaps.' Old Johannes Paso was a remarkable man, and seemed more so with age. He was now 79 years of age and was under the care of the parish Council for the Poor.

It was all so heartless, Johanna thought. Poor people were not really cared for. Former tenant farmers, whose families could not support them, were simply placed on farms within each parish. The Council for the Poor then contributed towards their upkeep. It paid very little, especially if the old ones could still do odd jobs. In her grandparents' case, Old Paso had been placed on one farm, while Maren, his wife, was placed on another some distance away. This was six years ago.

Still, Old Paso was not downhearted. He visited Maren often, and furthermore, he seemed to blossom. He had become very good at reading and writing. There was always a lump of charcoal in his pocket, and if he could get hold of some paper, wonderful pictures were sure to follow. He had a lively imagination, but drew mainly what he saw in nature. He drew goblins, elves and trolls too, as, like Johanna, they were not strangers to him. He drew the big animals of the forest, and if enough space was available on the paper, elks, lynx and even wolves would appear. Johanna had not seen any wolves. She had only heard their howls from Meitsjøen on winter's nights. What big, growly mouths they had.

Johanna would miss her grandfather very much when they left. He was sure to see them off. He might even come as far as Christiania. He was still amazingly fit and active – and so fond of his family.

Old Paso returned to Pasotorpet several times each year, to lend a hand with milking, to help bring in the hay or to do any small job that needed doing. The main reason, though, was to help the children with their reading. The catechism, which was always on the table, contained many difficult words and there was always much explaining to be done. Understanding of the proper faith ought to come early in life. And Johanna thought she had learned more from her grandfather than from the itinerant teacher. Perhaps that was why the pastor placed her as the head of the line, right up by the altar, on the Sunday of her confirmation. The whole congregation must have seen her there.

'I think he will come with us to Christiania,' she said aloud to the toy cone cow still in her lap. Her heart felt heavy. Unlike her father – and now her mother – she could not muster much enthusiasm for this place called Ny Seland. It was difficult to say goodbye to everything – to Grandfather, the animals, the blueberries, and the landscape she knew so well. And the little cottage where she felt so safe. Tears ran unnoticed down her cheeks. Still, Christian made it all possible. Thank God for dear Christian.

Who was Christian Christiansen from Steinbekken, now a farm worker at Skara? In the church records and on the emigration register, he is just a name. However, his now elderly grandchildren in New Zealand give a much fuller description. They also knew much of his youth. They sat on his lap when they visited him in Norsewood. Listened to his tales, watched his big worn hands and noticed his clear blue eyes that lit up as the stories grew.

Eileen Williams of Wellington, Ormond Andersen in Palmerston North, Joyce Otterson and Alex McCallum in Wanganui, Niel Andersen in Hamilton and Ena Dawn Christiansen in Auckland. Between them, they passed on many stories to me. Memories they all shared were their grandparents' very strong love for each other, and the realisation that had Christian gone to Canada, none of them would have existed.

One and a quarter centuries ago, and it is like yesterday. I can see Christian on his way from Steinbekken with his luggage, including Adolf's tool kit received in part-payment for the Canada ticket. Christian is on his way to Pasotorpet, where the people are almost ready to leave.

It was agreed that Christian would bring his belongings to Pasotorpet on the last Sunday in July. They would then take their baggage to Kuggerud farm, where they would join Johanna's older sister Berte Maria, her husband Ole and their two children, Anne and Arne. The party would travel together to the capital. It seemed doubtful that all their combined possessions could fit in one cart. The small children would also need a ride from time to time. Ole was to arrange the transport from Kuggerud. Other family groups would also leave Odalen over the next few days. Many horses and carts would make the same journey to Christiania to catch *Høvding* before the ship sailed. Surely, there would be extra space available somewhere.

Johan stood outside the cow byre at Pasotorpet. It was the last day of July 1873, the day before they were to leave. Everything was stowed on the cart, except the clothes they were to sleep in or would wear the next day. The byre was empty. The three cows, including the beloved Daisy, and most of the sheep and goats were sold. The unsold livestock were now salted and dried meat fated to accompany the family on its long journey. Only the horse remained, by arrangement with its new owner. It was grazing close to the cottage. Tomorrow Pasotorpet would be empty. The cottage, its worn benches and the heavy table would soon be all that remained to show that people had ever lived there. Of course, that was assuming anyone ever passed by and pushed open the door to look inside.

Shading his eyes, Johan looked to the end of the farmlet, to where the tall trees stood. All those heaps of stones! By God, he knew many of the big stones. He had battled with them. Struggled with them until he felt the taste of blood in his mouth. They were not the type to be picked up and thrown on the nearest heap. Oh no! They were obstinate beasts, well buried, and not willing to be lifted. He had fought them with spade and crow bar, and with his bare hands.

Stones . . . armies of them! The heaps were growing long before his time. His ancestors created them, and each generation had added to them. Yet the farmlet had not grown in size, or so it seemed. And where did they all come from? Every spring new ones appeared, even in patches cleared a century earlier. Did they multiply under the earth like potatoes?

He could still picture his father, small, bow-legged and with his back bent, struggling with yet another enemy. A blue rock of the worst kind. Johannes – Old Paso – eventually won. When the boulder was subdued and moved into place, the tired victor allowed himself a smile of triumph.

Today, the devils seemed to be smiling at Johan. Every heap of stones had a grin on its face. Wicked, evil smiles. We beat you in the end! Now you will leave us alone.

No, he had not given up. Not given in either. He was a toiler – the only difference was that in future he would toil elsewhere. There he would see some results, some return for his labours. Christoffer had said in his letter that Ny Seland's soil is so fertile there is no need of fertiliser. Just a few trees to be cleared away. And what is that compared with everlasting battles with stones? Big trees, but surely that would mean deep soil too. Not like Pasotorpet, where the soil was shallow, sandy and sour. Forty acres, Christoffer had said, of rich, fertile soil. Would the wealthy farmer at Skara have that much?

Johan had convinced himself he did not fear a new start in this new land. However, he was a little fearful of the voyage. He was a man of the forest, not a seaman, and he had never even seen the sea. Ny Seland was, he knew, at the other end of the earth – but perhaps the earth was quite small . . .

2 The long walk

THE atmosphere was hectic outside the cottage the next morning. Randi, carrying little Julius in her arms, attempted to pacify the grizzling Karen. The 7-year-old did not understand the events that surrounded her. Why had they emptied the house? Why was everything in boxes and bags, and packed on the cart?

Randi had repeatedly tried to explain to the child, who had smiled and nodded each time, and seemingly understood it all. Now, though, on the day of departure, it was obvious she had understood very little. Ny Seland, which they were supposed to visit, must be just beyond Kuggerud Farm. Why then, was it necessary to empty the cottage and put everything on the cart because of that?

Karen burst into tears and cried loudly when Randi explained they were not coming back to Pasotorpet.

'There, there, dear.' She stroked her daughter's hair tenderly with her free hand; the other hand clutching Julius to her breast. 'There, there, my darling. It will all work out. It's going to be very nice, everything. Much nicer than here at Pasotorpet.'

Words of comfort were of little help to Karen, but somehow they calmed Randi herself – a little. She felt strangely agitated and apprehensive this morning. There was no way back. She stood on the edge of the unknown. Some words of comfort, words to give her strength, were needed – even if she had to say them to herself. Could she believe her own words though? Would it really be much nicer where they were going? If not, it was sheer madness that Johan had started. And her brother, were the things he wrote true?

Nagging doubt and feelings of uncertainty underpinned her thoughts. When she discussed the future with Johan, when she dreamt and fantasized . . . Then, there was just longing for the new and better life. That was all they talked about. Johan would consider nothing else. There was no point in asking questions or contradicting him. Johan could see only a rich landscape, fields of grain, and animals grazing in big paddocks. And the imaginary house and barn were bigger than those at Skara or Nes.

Oh, she wanted to believe it all. Still this lingering uneasiness remained. Randi was very convincing when she told the children their plans. It all sounded so good. Meanwhile her heart wept silently. Her own doubts and fears remained well hidden.

Julius had influenced this. The innocent little creature, born last January, should not have been there at all. Ellen, born four years back and dead soon after her christening, had been followed to the same fate by a second little Ellen born the year before last. Randi had been convinced no more babies should be born at Pasotorpet in this generation. God moves in mysterious ways, though, and the will of the flesh is not easy to combat. Last summer she knew, once more, she was pregnant.

He was unwanted. Now, though, he was here, and nothing, nothing harmful must come to him. Her heart trembled when she thought of the two Ellens. God, please God, shield and protect little Julius. He was definitely the last one – her childbearing years were finished – and so he had seemed dearer to her than all the other children.

How would he travel aboard the ship? Across the oceans? Such a long way for this dear little baby. This responsibility, mixed with fear, weighing heavily upon her.

Randi was upset that she knew nothing of the type of domestic animals they had in Ny Seland. Her brother had not mentioned this – and it was so important. Were there goats there? Did they have sheep? Proper sheep that gave real wool. The spinning wheel. The blessed spinning wheel that spun and kept them in clothes. She wanted to take it with her anyway. This morning Johan had dismantled it carefully, piece by piece. Then he had tenderly wrapped it in the blankets they had slept in last night. It would travel safely, she felt, but would it be used again? Would it hum and sing as sweetly as it had done for so many years at Pasotorpet?

There was something very special about this spinning wheel. Of all her worldly goods, this was her dearest possession. She found it easy to spin wool that Johan had carded. She loved the stillness of the evenings when the spinning wheel hummed and Johan carded softly by the fireplace. The silence deepened and there was peace around her and within her. Then it was good to be alive and tomorrow no longer held any threats.

The spinning wheel stood for what was positive and good, for what was calming and brought peace of mind. She felt safer when she saw it carefully placed on top of the cart.

Little Karen calmed down, slowly. Her eyes, however, were still full of fear. She would not come home again and that frightened her. She could not laugh like her brother Fredrik, like her father too. And like Christian as well. They laughed so loudly as they roped everything together on the cart. Was that anything to laugh about? That they were never coming home again?

Laughter and loud voices. It may not have been entirely genuine, but it did ease the men's taut nerves a little. A quick-witted reply, boisterous manners, guffawing, all gave a brief sense of mastery, a moment of confidence – and the gnawing anxiety lessened.

Johan helped, knowingly or otherwise, with an anecdote about his parents, Johannes and Maren. 'Oh, the two of them. They knew the road to Christiania very well as they'd walked it both ways. It was just after the big fire, of April 1858. You were too young to remember that; when forty big shops in Christiania burnt down. Enough of that. They were to get a barrel of barley, which they carried back home – mother carrying almost half of it on her back. And she had her knitting as well. In fact, she knitted two sets of socks on the way.'

The two young men were greatly amused. This encouraged Johan to continue. 'They were quick walkers too. Got home at the same time as others who had a horse and had driven both ways. So I reckon we'll get there too – don't you?' There was laughter again, but this time it was more subdued and respectful.

'Of course we will Dad.' Fredrik had forgotten the gnawing feeling in his stomach. 'We are a strong family. Strong and ancient, and not afraid of starting out again in a new land.'

The horse, with care, made the first move. It knew the obstacles ahead. The load was heavy, the track stony and uneven, and the wheels at first unwilling to turn. With a groan, a bitter lament from the cart, it slowly moved away from Pasotorpet. Away from the place of poverty in the Skara forest.

Christian and the horse headed the little procession. Johan wanted it like that. The family gathered in silence a short distance from the grey cottage – Johan's arm around his wife's shoulders. There they farewelled their former world. Meanwhile, the clanking and clattering of the cart –

sound of its sturdy wheels on big stones – could be heard travelling down the hill. The family stood there for some time, even Karen, with everyone lost in their own feelings. Finally, Johan squeezed Randi's shoulder and silently indicated that it was time to get moving.

By the time the family began the long walk down the hill, the horse and cart could be neither seen nor heard. Johanna had a tight feeling around her chest, as if a metal band had been placed there. She turned several times over the next few minutes, and watched the grey cottage steadily shrinking in size. Her tears ran silently. She could not help herself.

When the cottage was finally out of sight, a feeling of great emptiness overwhelmed her. Emptiness and sadness. Gone was the excitement of a great adventure. Gone was the new life with Christian, and gone were the good feelings. Never again would she call the cows home for milking or feel the warmth of their bodies. Never again would she run barefoot here, or gather blueberries.

The family walked in deep silence. Johan led the way, now with little Julius in his arms. Next came Randi, holding Karen's hand, followed by the other children. Fredrik and Johanna were at the rear. Well-known landmarks surrounded them. They had just passed the Resting Rock. The giant silver birch was straight ahead. Then came the big anthill with the sour-sweet smell, at the foot of a fir tree. The ants that lived there were always busy, always building, always dragging fir needles along. And each summer, their cone-shaped home grew a centimetre or two. Then there was Meitsjøen, with its array of insects, low bushes and birds. It took a long time to pass the lake and to reach the next landmark – a cluster of pine trees with flaky red bark called the Six Sisters. These trees stood tall and straight and only had branches at the top.

Small puffs of wind broke the silence. Aspen leaves and small twigs stirred. The family became conscious of their own footsteps, their heavy boots against stone and gravel. The track had widened a little and they could tell they were catching up with Christian and the horse. The noise of the cartwheels as they ground against stone, steadily, steadily, made a tuneless song of its own. Then came a loud bang, a creaking sound, and then wood splintering. They could hear Christian's voice – loud and urgent.

Fredrik immediately ran ahead as fast as he could. Johan followed.

'Here, take Julius. Something has happened to the cart.' He pushed the baby into Randi's arms and set off. What the hell could have happened to the . . . O God, please forgive me – all our possessions. All our earthly goods are on that cart. We cannot have an accident here, before we are even halfway to Kuggerud Farm!

Christian looked apprehensively at the two men bearing down on him. Fredrik looked friendly enough, but not so his father. A quick inspection of the wheel calmed Johan. It was not as bad as he had feared. Only one of the four spokes had been broken by the mishap, although another looked a little bent and unhappy. The wooden rim, protected by its metal band, was still sound. But it would be impossible to continue on that wheel. And Kuggerud was still 5 kilometres away.

'Good thing we brought that extra wheel.' Johan had anticipated the likelihood of an accident happening. The men gathered slab stones to support the cart's weight, before beginning the lengthy business of changing the wheel. Randi and the children continued walking, so they at least could meet up with Berte Maria and Ole as arranged. The others would follow once the wheel was changed.

Kuggerud is a big farm today, just as it was in the 1870s. It borders the property owned by Hans Marius Trøseid, the local historian who proved so very helpful in the course of researching this book. The tarsealed road cuts through the fields of Kuggerud, just below and south of the main building. The road crosses the stream that begins at Meitsjøen and ends at Storsjøen (Great Lake). A little further on, a gravel sideroad branches off to the left. This, followed by several other sideroads, takes visitors almost to Pasotorpet today.

Don't imagine that the journey to Pasotorpet nowadays is easy, despite the network of gravel-covered logging tracks. The timber workers who return to the area every few years use these tracks, which are otherwise blocked by barriers. The correct turn-offs to Pasotorpet are also unmarked.

Walkers, despite maps and compasses, cannot guess where Pasotorpet is in the forest. I sought the help and guidance of Hans Marius' friend and neighbour, Bjørn Neskvern, who also had the key to the unfriendly barriers. These two, Bjørn and Hans Marius, proved mines of knowledge in every sense, and invaluable companions.

Standing on the tarsealed road, looking at the old Kuggerud homestead, one cannot help noticing the power poles, TV aerials, tractors and cars that are symbols of a different age. Yet it is not difficult to imagine the scene as it was a century and a quarter ago. For a few days, all doors were open – day and night – for emigrants who used the farm as their meeting place. The sympathetic hosts gave them a much-appreciated farewell. A farewell with dignity, in the form of hot meals and lodgings.

There was plenty of activity at Kuggerud. Four horses, each tethered to its own stake, grazed in the paddock nearest the house. There was plenty of lush grass here, with clover as well. Four large carts, arranged in a semicircle, stood behind the main house in the shade of the courtyard tree. Three were packed with travel goods, while the last, the newest-looking, was empty. This cart had built-in wooden benches on either side, each able to seat four adults or seven children. There was also a leather-covered padded seat at the front for the driver and two passengers. This cart was mostly meant for the children, but adults, tired from the long, hot and dusty walk to Christiania, would also rest on this cart from time to time.

Ole, bless him, had arranged all this. The horse and cart belonged to Kuggerud, where he had worked for the previous twelve months. The party had also been lent a driver, Gunnar, another farm worker who was a few years younger than Ole. Gunnar would bring the horse and cart back to Kuggerud.

A steady hum of voices dominated the scene. The heart-rending cry of a child could be heard, while another laughed so raucously its voice echoed off the barn wall. At least three families were present, all with children, at Kuggerud on this first day of August 1873. And, of course, the Paso family was coming, along with the bachelor Christian. The party planned to leave together, at daybreak the following morning. They would then board *Høvding* as soon as they reached the harbour.

The emigrants were not the only ones who had gathered at Kuggerud. Friends, relations and neighbours had come as well. Most came to give fond farewells, but others just came to stare. There was little laughter from the adults. Voices were low and the tone serious. Soft sobbing could also be heard. As more people arrived, children started separating themselves from the main group. They giggled, played games and enjoyed watching the large group of people.

A bow-legged old man with a white beard stood out from the rest as he moved quickly from group to group. He wanted a few words with so many people. He knew them all, old and young, and had slept in all their homes – thanks to Luther's catechism and his bits of charcoal. And everyone knew Johannes Johannesen – Old Paso.

Johan's older brother, Arne, and his wife Kari Amunds-datter, had also come with their children. They, along with some others from inner family circles, had decided to accompany the party to Christiania. It could not be helped that harvest time was nigh. It was not every day that close kin emigrated. When they were all safely aboard ship and its sails were unfurled, only then was it time for the final farewell. Those waving on the wharf could feel at that point, amongst other feelings, that all had been done correctly. Half the journey would already be over. The other half would be the responsibility of a good captain and a good ship. And Our Lord would see to that.

Old Paso had made up his mind. He had walked to Christiania before, admittedly long ago. Still, this time he would have nothing to carry, nothing that is but a heavy heart. The trip to the capital would go well. That he knew. Equally, he knew, the journey back would be difficult. Certainly it would be more difficult than the time he and Maren had carried the barrel of barley between them. That time he looked forward. This time he would look back, and he would continue to live his life thinking of those who had sailed away.

Johanna was overjoyed when she saw him. Small, bow-legged and a white beard, and unmistakably him – Grandpa. As tired as she was, Johanna ran the last 20 metres, her arms outstretched. He is still like a ferret, always alert with such quick movements, Randi thought. She smiled at the thought, from under her headscarf. She brought the rest of the children to their grandfather and, one by one, each received a hug.

'What have we here?' He had noticed the bundle at Randi's breast. 'A new little Paso? What could the name be?'

'Julius.'

'Julius, such a nice name too. You are sure to be strong, like your grandpa, and you'll manage the trip across the sea. I know you will.'

Across the sea! This was the source of Randi's fear. Crossing the sea with this tiny creature. Strong as Grandpa? What nonsense! How could anyone know what would happen at sea? And this dear little baby.

Despite his encouraging comments, Old Paso was full of fear. Not just for Julius. No, for everyone. He feared for the whole family. Their roots were deep in Mother Norway's soil. Could they form new roots? Would they really find what they were looking for? Old Paso, the philosopher, could not answer this. So he kept smiling and kept up words of encouragement, while inside, his old heart wept.

'You will have a good journey, I'm convinced of that. Remember, in the end there is only one Helmsman, only One who matters. Put your faith in Him. Our Lord will look after you, and not only across the sea.' Old Paso both looked and spoke as an old patriarch straight out of the Bible. His young disciples nodded, agreeing fully.

Randi looked from Julius to the patriarch and back again. She felt better. 'You are so right. Only then can we feel safe.'

Berte Maria and Ole had spotted them and were moving towards them as well. Their boy Arne grizzled as he clung to his mother's skirt. Meanwhile, their daughter, Anne – Berte Maria's oldest child, born out of wedlock – had offered her rag-doll to little Karen. The two girls started playing. Although much the same age, they did not know they were auntie and niece. They whispered to each other with such confidence and were already sharing secrets with the rag-doll. Karen forgot the fear that had burdened her all day. She had a new friend and they were going to travel together. There were so many children here. It was going to be fun.

Ole looked questioningly at his mother-in-law. 'Johan will be here shortly,' she said with calmness in her voice. 'It was just the wheel. You know how stony the track is up to our place. Could hardly expect anything else. Thank goodness they brought an extra wheel with them. You know how Johan always anticipates, looks ahead. He's very good at that.'

Old Paso caught the anxious look in Ole's eyes, and thought it was time he cheered everyone up. He could assure them – and knew from personal experience – that from now on the road was very good. No more boulders of bluestone or grey-stone. Oh no, just smooth and even all the way, and it got wider too, near Christiania. Three, even four, carts could travel side by side. He concluded with a determined nod of the head, 'Thank God. The worst is over!'

Randi was keen to catch up on the latest news. Had Karen and Ole made up their minds? Were there other relations from Odalen who might travel with them across the sea? She had seen and knew all of those who had assembled at Kuggerud, but Johan's sister and her husband were not amongst them. She knew the names of Karen Johannesdatter and Ole Christoffersen and their four children were entered in the Register of Emigration. She also knew her sister-in-law, like she herself, had been very much in two minds over emigrating – and had openly voiced her doubts. Ole, however, had been as enthusiastic as Johan, despite lacking his brother-in-law's doggedness and persistence.

'Who won in the end?'

'Karen gave in suddenly. Then there was such urgency about everything. They could not wait and so they took off yesterday. "We'll see you aboard *Høvding*", they said.'

Johan's older brother, Arne, married to Kari Amundsdatter, had also seriously considered emigrating. Shall we, or shall we not? He agonised over this. As it turned out there had been no need for this deep and hard thinking. When his wife understood what it was all about she took control.

'We are too old and the child is too young. So, forget about it. What luck it was that we didn't lose her straightaway. It would be sheer madness if we exposed her now to the hazards of travelling and all that.'

The girl, Rangdi, was a strong, healthy 1-year-old. A bonny child indeed. Admittedly, when born prematurely last year, she had at first been small and weak, but only for a start. Kari bristled with protection for her child.

'We got the child back from Him once before and He would never forgive us if we did anything reckless now. The sea is very dangerous Arne. And you should thank God that you were spared that time. Have you forgotten that?'

No, Arne had not forgotten. There was no chance to forget – even if he had been far too small to remember the day. He had heard the story so many times he could see all the gruesome details anyway. That Sunday morning, Whitsunday 1822. On the very day he was christened, the old wooden church at Grue had gone up in flames. The panic inside the burning building! The dreadful inferno! The tragic loss of 113 lives was the reason Norway's churches could now only be built of brick or stone and their doors must open outwards. Even the churches themselves re-minded him almost daily of the tragedy he had survived.

Oh yes, Arne felt he was there, and had truly been through it all. That someone had thrown him out the window, in his new christening gown, and that he was not hurt. He remembered it very clearly. And he should be eternally thankful to God for having been spared. That was well understood. It may well have been his Heavenly Father who threw him out the window in the first place.

'You are quite right, Kari, we must stay behind for the child's sake. For the child's sake.' He had placed due emphasis on those words. Everyone would surely understand it was because of Rangdi. No one should believe his wife bullied him. It was just good sense that had prevailed, coupled with Christian gratitude.

Today, though, with all the hustle and bustle at Kuggerud, and surrounded by people prepared to start a new life, today he was in a state of turmoil. It did not help to look at his sister-in-law, Randi, standing ready to travel with weak little Julius in her arms. Arne could not help casting a glance at Kari, who held their child as if she were a baby. Rangdi was much bigger and so strong. There was no need to hold her either. She was quite able to stand on her own two sturdy legs. Arne felt regret, and was torn in all directions. How weak he had been.

Johanna sensed the tension in her uncle. 'You may follow

before long, when we know exactly what Ny Seland has to offer. I promise to write to you.' Arne was grateful for those few words, but Kari snorted, tossed her head in the air and looked away. She took a firmer grip on her little daughter.

Johan and Fredrik, the horse and cart and Christian had all appeared. Ole had already found a suitable piece of oak and the men set about repairing the wheel. Two new spokes were needed. It was good to work together. Both brothers – Arne and Johan – knew it was the last time they would do so.

The daylight was fading. The evening meal had been eaten in the big kitchen at Kuggerud. The womenfolk had made up beds in the barn and had settled the children for the night. Meanwhile, the men had gathered by the courtyard tree, some standing, and some sitting. Some smoked pipes, some chewed tobacco. Dusk deepened. The summer night slowly closed in. All wanted to hear once more of the Swede who had passed through Odalen last year. Ole Olsen knew all about the well-dressed gentleman who had been sent from Ny Seland to offer land and hard work to future emigrants.

'Free land, was that it? Well yes,' said Ole slowly, with a nod of his head. 'There is a little to pay, but that's later. Nothing in advance. And well-paid work. That's what he said. So we can all get off to a good start.'

'Nothing more to pay for the journey? No. Nothing except that pittance to show we were serious about going. Ny Seland is paying for everything else. There is plenty of money in Ny Seland, but they want good workers. That's how he put it. They will lend us the money if needed.' Ole broke into Swedish to sound more convincing. 'And you pay back the loan over a long time.'

'You should have seen him. Such a fine fellow. He had a hat, a black cape, and a black suit too, with tight trousers. A shiny white shirt with the collar turned up at the corners.' He painted a very detailed picture. 'And would you believe it, he even wore white gloves and on his feet he had shiny black shoes, more suited for dancing than for walking.'

It was hard to believe. He must have been very wealthy?

'After five years in Ny Seland, he had all he needed in life – so he said.' There was a long silence, giving the men of the forest time to contemplate life in black cape, white gloves and hat.

'I believe him,' Ole said, breaking the silence. 'Why should he lie? He will be on the wharf to meet us, no doubt about that. He will help us settle in. Find work for us, and show us the land we have been given. Oh no, he was telling the truth all right. After all, he is going to be a farmer too, and will be our neighbour.'

Ole was right. The Swede, Bror Eric Friberg, had six blocks of land – some 105 hectares – at Makotuku, the farthest end of Norsewood's Scandinavian Block.

The conversation continued until the men pulled their worn boots off and went to sleep in the barn. This was their last night secure in a familiar environment – the night of 1 August 1873.

Three days later a large caravan of horses, carts and people approached the capital. Others had joined the families from Odalen. Some came from Aurskog, Rakkestad and Borge, a handful from Kongsvinger and lastly, a large contingent from Fredrikstad and Halden. Still, those from Odalen were the largest group. All the families seemed blessed with many children. There were also a small number of unmarried people. Young men and even young girls who had chosen to start a new life in this new land. Each had one thing in common – poverty. All they possessed was now heaped on these carts and drays that increasingly squeaked and groaned their way towards the harbour. It was a hot and dusty August afternoon.

A gasp of astonishment rippled through the party as each group in turn emerged from the Lo Valley. Next followed a whisper – 'the sea, the sea' – from the long line of tired walkers.

In the distance they could see Akershus castle, and there, finally, was the ocean. And there, a little to the left of the castle, was a ship – just one among many – its tall, thin masts reaching for the sky. Could it be *Høvding*? Johanna thought it was dangerously small. How could a tiny thing like that house them all, and their belongings too? How could it get across the sea, a toy like that, without sinking under the weight of all the people and all these cartloads of belongings?

As they drew nearer, though, *Høvding* grew in size. Johanna saw that the three masts were as thick and tall as the biggest trees in the Skara forest, and surrounding them was a deck big enough, perhaps, for thirty Paso cottages. Well, maybe not that many. But, yes, indeed, there will be room for us all.

Johan was impressed. He stopped as he entered the wharf and wiped the sweat from his face with his sleeve. Two carts were unloaded ahead of the Paso people. A big, solid-looking person with a reddish, somewhat furrowed face, seemed to be directing operations. 'This way, nearer the gangway. A little closer still. Stop!' Then he came over to the Paso family. He had a good honest face and untidy hair – and did not look dangerous.

'Olassen's my name. Second mate, on board. My job is to look after the passengers and their belongings.' He stopped there, looking at his new charges, at their tired horse and their crude farm cart, all covered in dust. Poor devils, in their old, worn clothes, looking lost and inquisitive at the same time.

'Put your things there, over by the gangway at the middle of the ship. My crew will take it aboard. Get the horse and cart away from the wharf area. Others are coming.' Johan nodded. He understood it all. Olassen spoke Norwegian, but with a singsong tone, and his voice had not been unfriendly.

The second mate marched off. Other groups needed his guidance. Poor devils, once more, they also looked so miserable. Do they know what they are letting themselves in for?

It did not take Johan, Fredrik and Christian long to unload the cart, and immediately a group of the ship's crew was there, forming a human chain. Soon everything was travelling smoothly from hand to hand, up the gangway, along the deck, through a hatch well forward, and up into the cargo compartment close to the anchor chains. However, when they came to the blankets containing the spinning wheel, Johan gave his orders.

'Careful there boys, so you don't damage the wife's equipment.' With that, the young seamen from Tønsberg laughed and proceeded to handle the blanket bundles with exaggerated care, and amidst giggles and smart remarks, passed them down the line as if they were living babies. They had the same singsong speech as Olassen, as if the wind had rearranged the sounds of the words. Johan did not hear what they said, but he knew they were laughing at him. He felt hot and flustered, and turned away. Thoughtless young boys! They did not know that they were handling a precious thing, a spinning wheel that spun wool and made clothes. He would forgive them, though. They knew no better. He chose not to give them a piece of his mind. They were young and ignorant, and they were all going to be together for many weeks. Johan bent down to the chest he had kept aside. This one contained the precious dried and smoked meat, crispbread and cheeses, and that way no one could see he was hurt.

'This is not to go with the cargo. It's to be where we're sleeping. Here Fredrik. You too, Christian. Lift!' He used a strong voice now, full of authority, to cover the awkwardness he really felt.

'Certainly,' Christian understood everything. He knew that his future father-in-law was hurt. 'But where shall we put the chest?'

Johan hesitated. The second mate was nowhere to be seen. Perhaps he could ask some of the crew up on the deck? Certainly, there were no passengers around from whom he could enquire. Hesitatingly, he took a few steps up the shaky gangway.

'Where do you think you are going!' It sounded like thunder, loud and angry. Captain Nordby was on deck, a short man, with incredibly wide shoulders. Square and massive-looking, Nordby was an undersized troll of a man. Huge, red, furry hands gripped the railing, and his square-shaped head and angry mouth resembled those big ugly fish in Meitsjøen. The seamen had vanished. They sensed their captain was approaching and were suddenly very busy on the deck below.

The captain had no time for these poverty-stricken people. Farm workers from the interior, with dirt under their fingernails, who didn't even pay their own way. He snorted contemptuously. Where was Olassen? Had he not passed on the order that no one was to come aboard before 12 August? No one! And here was this miserable creature trying to board the ship, walking up his gangway – and looking as if he was going to his own cowshed. The cheek of it.

Johan was thunderstruck at the sight of this, but managed in the end to convey his question.

This time it was the Captain who was near speechless. 'Where will you sleep? Sleep, you said? What has that got to do with me? Find your own place! You know where I would like you to go?' He was silent for a moment, then cupped his furry hands and bawled out in a voice that could have been heard over a raging cyclone, so that half of Christiania could hear.

'No one comes aboard this ship before I give the order!'

That was enough for this rabble. He turned on his heel and stormed off towards his cabin. If the farmers and landowners they had just deserted had not taught this mob manners and respect, then he would do it!

Johan was shocked and deeply hurt. Christian, Fredrik and all the others who witnessed the exchange felt much the same. This was not a good omen for the future.

3 'The sea, the sea'

O LE and Karen did not get the chance to pass on a warning to the others. Along with Jacob Isaksen and his wife Karen, they had reached Christiania the day before, and had heard the bad news. Nobody could board the ship at this stage. Its sailing date was now set at 13 August. At 12 noon on the previous day, all passengers were to assemble at the big shed on the wharf. Roll call would then take place and the passenger list would be drawn up. All bookwork would be done at the same time – and no latecomers could join the ship after that. These were the orders. All straightforward and simple. But where were they to stay until then? To that question, the captain had simply shrugged his shoulders. That was not his problem. The ship was not a lodging house or hospice.

Ole Christoffersen was devastated. He certainly had no money for lodgings, and everything was so expensive in the capital. Jacob Isaksen's predicament was the same. Between them, they had a few shillings – hardly enough for one night. To sleep in the open, along with their wives and six children – all of whom were on the verge of tears? Oh no! They had hoped to be the first to board, and install their families in a good, comfortable part of the ship. And now this calamity!

Karen felt she'd had a premonition that something awful would happen, even before leaving home. Now it had happened, straightaway. She was right, wasn't she? Still, she kept that to herself, instead saying in a meek little voice: 'Where shall we sleep tonight, Ole? Can you tell me that?' She bent her head and prayed silently. Ole could tell her nothing. He just stood there moping.

It was obvious that Jacob and Karen had argued, and were equally bereft of positive ideas. Just when the four adults felt completely overwhelmed by their situation, Ole had spotted the men in grey coats and black hats. They were just outside the wharf area, moving from group to group. And they seemed to be handing out food. The Home Mission was in action, attempting to help the homeless and the destitute. Lately emigrants had needed assistance too, people who were waiting for ships, and had run out of food and money.

Ole plucked up courage. Could they help with lodgings for poor emigrants stranded in the big city?

The Home Mission did indeed come to their rescue. This was the answer to Karen's silent prayer. Their hospice was only a stone's throw away, just to the east of Akershus castle. And not only did it take in Ole and Jacob and their families, but it also took in all the emigrants from Solør and Odalen who arrived the next day. And the payment? No set price at all. Only what people were able to pay.

Ole was very pleased with himself. He walked about and checked the straw mattresses on the floor. He had found accommodation for half of Odalen it seemed. So handy and so inexpensive too.

In spite of this, there was no festive atmosphere in the hospice when they were all safely installed. So many had witnessed the dreadful dressing down poor Johan had received from the captain – and the rest heard about it later.

They were frightened. How would they fare on a ship with a captain like that? And for many weeks? Had he not also alluded that Johan should go to Hell? A disgusting, godless man for sure. Would it be safe to put their lives in his hands?

The Odalen people sat in small groups on their straw-filled mattresses until well into the night of 4 August. They were deep in discussion on these and other disturbing questions. Now and then a corner of a shawl whisked away a few tears. The children sat close by and showed no inclination to play.

A resolution was made that night. No matter how rude the captain was, or how he might behave in the future, the families from Solør and Odalen would stick together. They would go down to the wharf in one solid group just before midday on 12 August. They would go aboard together, and would try to get sleeping quarters as near to each other as possible.

Johan, who had been humiliated and still felt this deeply, was fully in favour of this decision. 'We must support each other, the whole time. If we do that, it will all turn out well. Don't let him frighten us. We may not see much of him anyway. It's Olassen, the second mate, who is our man. Let's forget about Captain Nordby.'

In spite of these fine sentiments, Johan had a restless night. All his visions for the future had become clouded. Now troubled thoughts kept returning to the question of guilt. If things went wrong? If Randi and the children were to suffer? If the agent from Ny Seland had lied to them? If the ship sank? If, if, if . . .

It was entirely his fault. He had led his whole family into this, and others too, perhaps. There would be punishment awaiting him in the next world. That could only mean Hell. Did the captain know something he didn't?

He heard people tossing and turning. Rustling noises came from the straw mattresses lying in straight lines on the floor. Others too, must be sleeping fitfully, plagued by similar bad thoughts. Eventually Johan fell asleep, but the tug-of-war between hope and guilt continued in his tired brain.

The well-wishers were also installed at the Mission Hospice, and the would-be emigrants now lived on the food of those who had come to farewell them. Dried and salted meat, ham and cheeses and other food belonging to the emigrants, must remain intact. Food aboard ship was supposed to be good, so it was said. Still, you could never know for sure, and with a captain like that! In any case, it was prudent to have something in reserve.

Old Paso lost no time in gathering up the children. He had a natural ability to establish contact with the young and small, so it was not difficult. Perhaps it was the other way round – the children were instinctively drawn to him. He was a storyteller and a mimic, and could take several parts in his many tales. He spoke with his arms, shoulders and eyes as well. He knew of the animals in the forest, trolls, and the invisible world. He knew his Bible too, or rather, he knew the four Gospels, the fourth best of all. The rest was a little confusing and somehow didn't tally with what Jesus had said.

There was an air of urgency about Old Paso this week in Christiania. So much to be passed on in a short time. The young ones needed their mental baggage, not just for the journey, but for life. Old Paso foresaw that the parents would be very busy in their next chapter of life. There would be so many new things to learn, so much to absorb, perhaps different ways of thinking. Another language to master. The parents would have little time to pass on ancestral knowledge.

Today, he had the children seated in a semicircle on the ground outside the hospice. It was mid-morning on 12 August, the day before *Høvding* was to sail. Some adults also joined in to hear what Old Paso had to say. Johanna was there too, with Christian at her side. Old Paso had no further tales to tell. He cleared his throat and looked serious.

'You are travelling a long way. So far that none of you

may ever come back. However, don't forget where you came from. Remember there was more than just poverty and hardship. You have ancestors who gave you life. You also have a heritage. Knowledge is the lightest burden to carry through life, and it's the most important one as well. Shoulder that burden.'

Old Paso looked up. Others had joined the group of listeners, however, he did not recognise them. His vision was a little blurred. Like his audience, he was touched by his own words. Some snivelled audibly.

Christian found Johanna's hand and pressed it re-assuringly. He had never before felt so close to her. When she wept, and she was doing that now – silently – he felt she needed support, protection. He felt that he should give it to her, he and no one else. Warm waves went through his body when he felt her squeeze his hand in return. The warmth penetrated every fibre of his body, leaving him feeling wonderfully dizzy. He felt so light-headed he almost forgot to listen to the old man.

Old Paso had produced his Bible and, while turning its pages, concluded his farewell speech. 'I know you all have the same wish. That you will be better off in the future than you were in the past. That's my wish for you too. Still, don't forget it's up to you to shape your own world, through sweat and hard work. Nothing comes easily in this world. Nothing free, nothing gratis – only through hard work, and guidance from above.'

At last, he found the passage he sought: John, chapter 15, verses 12 to 18.

> 12   *This is my commandment, That ye love one another, as I*
> *have loved you.*
> 13   *Greater love hath no man than this, that a man lay*
> *down his life for his friends.*
> 14   *Ye are my friends, if ye do whatsoever I command you.*
> 15   *Henceforth I call you not servants; for the servant*

> *knoweth not what his lord doeth: but I have called you*
> *friends; for all the things that I have heard of my Father*
> *I have made known unto you.*
> 16 *Ye have not chosen me, but I have chosen you and*
> *ordained you, that ye should go and bring forth fruit,*
> *and that your fruit should remain: that whatsoever ye*
> *shall ask of the Father in my name, he may give it to you.*
> 17 *These things I command you, that ye love one another.*
> 18 *If the world hate you, ye know that it hated me before it*
> *hated you.*

Old Paso's voice had been firm and clear. He closed his Bible to show that the sermon was over. The adult listeners whispered a soft 'Amen', raised their heads again and began to slowly drift away. Johanna, however, let go of Christian's hand and ran to Old Paso.

'Grandpa, Grandpa!' Not attempting to hide her tears anymore, she threw her arms around his neck and sobbed.

After a while, Old Paso lifted her chin with his trembling, work-worn hand. 'I hold no fears for you, dear child. I know that you, Johanna, will do the right things in life wherever you are. Because of this, when I am home again and think of you, I shall be at peace with myself. Think of me like that. Not with heartache, but instead with peace in my soul.'

When everyone had left, Christian coughed discreetly, cleared his throat and plucked up courage. 'Come now Johanna, it's time for roll call.'

It was late in the afternoon of 13 August. *Høvding* was finally on its way, but ever so slowly. The fiord had been very calm, like polished glass, all morning. A few puffs of wind around midday allowed the captain to bellow out his orders, and all sails were set.

For the passengers, it was of little importance whether the wind blew or not. With months ahead of them aboard the ship, reaching Ny Seland a few hours earlier or later mattered very little. Captain Nordby saw things differently. He was also out of sorts today. Admittedly, it was good to be at sea again. To hear water splashing, albeit softly, against the side of the ship. Good to give orders and good to be in charge. In other words, it was good to feel at home.

In spite of that, as he stood aft by the wheelhouse with second mate Olassen and the helmsman, the expression on his face conveyed deep concern. The erratic breeze filled the sails occasionally and then left them limp. Watching all the manoeuvring with keen eyes, he also wondered what he should say to the passengers. He would stop any insubordination instantly, and the thought of the speech he planned darkened his brow.

What a hell of a cargo he had this time! Timber or grain would stay in its place, obediently and silently, but a load of humans? Miserable and poor at that – and from the interior! And who thought they were on a picnic. Damn it all!

Anger had grown increasingly within him since yesterday. Since the confrontation with that Christiania farmer, Elliot Greiner. Who the hell did he think he was? Daring to make demands the moment he got aboard. Being big, strong and loud, or with huge swinging arms like a gorilla, won't help him here! Not against Captain Carl Nordby. This ape of a farmer may well be angry because the town has taken his land – but so what?

He also thought of that little farmer from the interior, the one with the felt pants who had tried to sneak aboard a week early. He recognised him yesterday when he arrived with his tribe of children. He looked surly, defiant, and almost as if he didn't like to be spoken to. Both these fellows, and any others with unsavoury ideas, had better be put in their place. A firm lesson given straightaway would ensure they understood who was in charge.

Two days passed before the lesson could be given. They had reached Son, only halfway down the Christiania Fiord. The breeze had then dropped away altogether. The sails were furled and orders given to drop the anchor. The crew took this calmly. They were used to it. The emigrants, though, had started to show signs of impatience. Would they ever reach Ny Seland at this rate?

The feeling that complaints regarding the ship's speed were imminent gave Nordby his chance. Most passengers were on deck, forward of the main hatch, when they heard the anchors fall. The captain had an important announcement to make – and this was the perfect opportunity.

Johan was apprehensive. All strength drained from him as the anchor chains raced out with an ear-splitting noise. The heavy splash of the anchors left him feeling powerless. He anticipated the worst and guessed it was linked to the episode on the wharf the day before their departure. The clash had occurred as he waited in the shed to have his name entered on the passenger list. The stern-looking captain did the roll call and entered the names, while the ship's doctor, Mogstad, standing at the door nearest the gangway, checked the passengers' state of health. As they passed, he studied the backs of their hands for a moment, then looked in their eyes and asked them to poke out their tongues. That was it. No one failed his or her medical test.

'Next please!'

Second mate Olassen had then escorted the families onto the ship, down the wide ladder at the main hatch amidships, and along the next deck going aft. There, on both sides of the centre passage, were the passengers' sleeping quarters. Unmarried men occupied the first section, the one nearest the main hatch. Then came the big section for families, and further back, towards the stern, was the small section for single women. Tarpaulins, stretched tautly, divided these three parts. Smaller tarpaulins lay in heaps in the centre passage, where the families were to sleep. These were for general use and were intended to allow families to rig up their own 'room dividers', to create some privacy. The two smaller sections, for single men and women, had no extra tarpaulins. However, they had one piece of luxury. They had bunks. These were arranged, two-high, along the sides of the ship. Single people received extra blankets to allow them some privacy. These could be hung across the front of the bunks while they slept.

The big section for families contained large heaps of straw mattresses. Children were expected to sleep top to tail. However, an unmistakable smell revealed that many of the mattresses were moist, and this had upset the passengers.

When the burly farmer from Christiania discovered this, he had stormed back to the shed on the wharf. He took the gangway in two strides, his anger rising. He had a few questions for the captain.

Elliot Greiner made his dissatisfaction clear. Had he not paid half the trip in advance? He had not done this to have his wife, four children and himself sleep in such an evil-smelling open space. His contract stated that his family was to have a cabin to itself. What sort of cheating was this? He waved his big arms in the air to underline these points, to the extent that people nearest the captain backed away in fear.

Not so the captain. Instead, he stood there, feet well apart, head thrust forward, and his huge shoulders hunched like a bull ready to charge. Giving no outward sign of being taken by surprise, he glared back at the farmer.

'How dare you! You have a cheap economy ticket, just like the rest of these workhouse inmates. Demanding privileges? What audacity!' He had raised his voice and thrust his upper body further forward, as if ready to gore his attacker. 'You go ashore now, if that's what you want. We don't want troublemakers. At sea, I arrest troublemakers – just so you know!'

Greiner had to eat humble pie. He tried pointing out clauses in the contract, which said that officers were to listen to complaints from the passengers. They were to discuss them with the complainants and a reasonable solution was to be reached.

'Here I reach the solutions,' the captain snorted. 'On the ship, my words are law.' He then abruptly turned to the next family to be entered on the passenger list. He looked composed, but was boiling inside. Paid for half the journey? What nonsense. Thirty-six shillings had been placed on the table, not a penny more. Moreover, the balance owing had been entered against his name on the passenger list, £35 sterling it said, there in the margin. Didn't the idiot know the difference between Norwegian shillings and pounds sterling? And that was only a third of the total cost anyway. The Ny Seland Government paid the rest, so they could get this roistering rabble into slavery quickly.

Hearing this verbal cannonade shocked Johan deeply. He became anxious too, as there was not a single shilling left in his pocket for him to put on the table. And what was this about a contract? He had not seen one. He'd been told that the voyage was free. His heart pounded with trepidation as he approached the captain.

'Johan Johannesen, with wife and four children.'

'Where do you come from? Odalen.' The captain supplied the answer himself. 'Owing £60 sterling? Do you know how much that is? It will take many years of slavery to pay that off.'

Once more Johan felt humiliated, but kept his mouth closed. Instead he looked away, his face set hard, and began assisting Randi and the children with their hand luggage. The helpful second mate met them by the gangway. Olassen cleared his throat. He wanted to get an important message across, but this was difficult without hurting these unfortunate people.

'You have not been at sea before. You cannot know what it is like, or understand what the sea demands of us and of you.' Not a very promising introduction he thought. Better jump right into it. 'Some people speak of a contract. Some have seen it and some have signed it. I just wanted to say straightaway . . . forget about these contracts.'

Captain Nordby had mounted the octagonal platform surrounding the main mast. There he stood, square, solid, in command and full of importance, like a feudal lord surveying his villeins. People who had obediently appeared when they heard the anchors fall, now packed the aft deck where they milled about uneasily. Big Greiner was in the front row, hands on hips, not intimidated, and ready to oppose or ask questions if the captain proved difficult. The captain must stick to the contract. That was all, and that meant showing respect to passengers.

Force and high-handed action fostered resentment. That, Elliot Greiner knew better than most. He had fought the town authorities for years over his land and his rights, and had lost. Greiner hated being pushed around or trampled on, and if the captain proposed to do that, then – clenching his fists – the captain would regret it one day.

Carl Nordby's eyes wandered slowly across the upturned faces, some serious, some apprehensive, some defiant, some just plain stupid. My God, what a miserable lot. Just below him was the landless gorilla farmer, looking angrier than the rest. Perhaps he should modify his language a little because this landless ape felt sorry for himself. Obviously he had studied the contract, and the fine print as well. A brief lesson regarding duties and behaviour aboard ship was, however, essential.

'When at sea, this ship becomes a little community. A society in miniature. And like all societies, it will fall apart without rules. We shall never reach port, never reach our destination – if the rules are not respected! It is the captain's job, and his alone, to ensure that this occurs.' Quite a useful introduction. The captain was pleased with himself. Squaring his massive shoulders, he raised his head and his voice to ensure that all could hear.

'The rules of the sea cannot be written in a contract. They change from day to day and from week to week, depending on the weather, the sun, the sea and the wind. I have the responsibility to decide what will apply at any time. Therefore, as long as we are at sea, my word is law. Remember that.' He looked around at the faces and focused momentarily on Greiner's hard, cold and angry eyes. Then he repeated, slowly and with due emphasis on every syllable: 'My word will be law!'

Nordby still felt it necessary to spell things out even more clearly. Some people might still harbour rebellious tendencies, this landless, landlubber farmer especially. A little fright might allude to the power at his disposal, even if it hit everyone and seemed needlessly brutal.

'We have a lock-up on board, a police cell, and my duties include using it if necessary. Anyone who opposes me, who complains, or who disobeys my orders will be placed under arrest. Bear this in mind – and remember that you have had fair warning.'

The captain, whose height was somewhat less than average, had looked eight-feet-tall and had spoken with great authority. He now turned on his heel and with much dignity, descended from the platform. Elliot Greiner had opened his mouth several times during the lecture, as if to protest, but no sound came forth. He stood there speechless like everyone else.

The emigrants had been dealt with and were now swept from the captain's mind. He ordered the lighter to be lowered and rowed ashore. This was his chance to bid farewell to some of his old skipper friends, who were sure to be there. While on land, he would also take the opportunity to buy duty-free tobacco, as Son was the only 'Free Port' remaining on the eastern side of the Christiania Fiord. Tobacco could be obtained at bargain prices here. And good money could be made from selling it in small quantities to tobacco-starved passengers. The emigrants might be poor, but these cunning peasants would have a few shillings tucked away. A few cases of spirits would also come in handy, although this was not for the passengers. Definitely not! Such an undisciplined lot would go berserk if they had access to alcohol. Small quantities could be bought, of course. Strictly for medical use, but not whole bottles. That would be madness.

Cognac, rum and whiskey were mainly reserved for himself and for Mogstad, the ship's doctor. They could socialise when the wind was fair and steady, enjoy a cigar, have a glass or two – *Skål* – and hold an intelligent conversation. Their discussions were on topics well beyond the comprehension of peasants and landlubbers. It was important to stay mentally stimulated – alert and refreshed – on these long trips.

Doctor Mogstad, too, had his own cabin and welcomed visits from the captain. His library was not well stocked. And his days could be long, as he did not believe in holding open clinic aboard ship. Nor did he believe in having patients coming to his cabin. He did not want them arriving, day or night, and disturbing him with minor or imaginary complaints. He was, of course, prepared to receive patients, but notice should come through second mate Olassen.

Captain Nordby, all unpleasantness forgotten the moment he stepped into the lighter, looked forward to a few hours among friends. Several old colleagues had swallowed the anchor here. They now occupied sun-drenched houses clustered on a hillside above the wharf, all of them painted white and decorated with small gardens.

Son was a seafarers' village, and seemed mainly reserved for old captains. It provided easy access to the small luxuries of life, and here too, one could stay in contact with ships and the sea. Some old sea dogs had also appointed themselves pilots. They assisted ships bound for Christiania that, regardless of weather, needed this service. Was that the tall, thin and straight shape of old Captain Thorvaldsen he could see parading on the wharf and shading his eyes while looking out to sea? My God, it looked like Thor Thorvaldsen, the old saltwater buccaneer.

The five friends enjoyed a lively evening at the small pub. Tobacco smoke hung thick and blue under the low ceiling, and rum flowed like water. Tales, tall and even taller, combined with laughter that rumbled like waves breaking on the shore. *Høvding*'s cargo caused concern as well as merriment.

'Slaves, poor devils, or cannibal fodder,' said one. He had sailed past Fiji in the 1850s and knew what he was talking about. 'The natives in New Zealand are of the same ilk – a bloodthirsty lot. The emigrants will discover that. Poor devils!'

It was late evening before *Høvding*'s captain returned. He struggled somewhat with the ladder and to get his purchases safely aboard. With a little help from his two rowers, all went well, in the end.

The passengers regained their power of speech when they saw Captain Nordby depart in the lighter. They remained on deck until sunset. Small groups sat on the main hatch or simply stood around, deep in their various discussions. Two points emerged in the end – that Elliot Greiner from Christiania would be their spokesman if future conflicts arose and – a question – where was their cook? Had anyone seen the cook?

4 The unwanted passenger

A steady easterly breeze blessed *Høvding* the next day. Most passengers were on deck when they passed Ferder lighthouse around midday. They remained on deck, clutching the railing on the starboard side, to catch the last glimpses of their homeland. For all they knew, none would ever see it again. Some passengers claimed to have seen Sweden on the port side, and perhaps that was even the tip of Jutland?

Second mate Olassen conveyed an important message to Mr Greiner. Would he care to call at the captain's cabin at two-bells? By that time, they would be safely out into the North Sea.

The Christiania farmer was dumbfounded. What could this be about? Still, he had time to discuss the situation with Christian. Misunderstandings and conflicts were best cleared up face to face, so surely nothing but good could come from this visit. 'Keep calm. Don't lose your temper,' Christian advised.

'Enter.' The captain's voice sounded more like a gunshot. Elliot bent low to pass through the door. Inside he found a smiling, friendly-looking captain. He appeared relaxed and was seated in an armchair by a low mahogany table.

'Do sit down Mr Greiner, here in the comfortable chair. May I offer you a tot of rum?' With great expertise he fished out two glasses and a bottle in one sweeping movement and placed them on the table.

'No thank you. Never touch the stuff. However, you go ahead and *Skål* with yourself.' Goodness me. I could have put that better. Not very polite at all, thought Greiner. The captain did indeed go ahead. After the second glass, he wiped his mouth with the back of his hand.

'Hmm, not liking a little rum. Strange. But of course, I respect your position.'

Respect! Respect – what did the captain know of respect? Respect only for himself, for money, for power and for the ruling class. Would he ever know that respect was a two-way thing? Be polite. Don't lose your temper – but Elliot felt the anger rising within him. He remembered his father, who was released from jail in 1855. A close friend of Marcus Thrane, Greiner senior succumbed to tuberculosis soon after. Although only 11 years old at the time, much of the family responsibility had fallen upon Elliot's young shoulders. Marcus Thrane had become his role model. A visionary. A fearless fighter for the oppressed and for justice, Thrane had stood up to arrogant authority.

Marcus Thrane (1817-1890) was leader of Norway's first labour movement, called 'thranitterbevegelsen' (the thranitt movement). This movement worked to free and to organise Norwegian labourers, whose lot in life at that time was extremely harsh. This was Norway's first organised political mass movement. The son of a former director of the Rigsbanken (a state bank) who had been caught embezzling, Thrane had grown up stigmatised by his father's wrongdoing. He became a teacher and then a newspaper editor, but was sacked when the subscribers objected to his socialist views.

The same year (1849) Thrane started his own newspaper, Arbeiderforeningens Blad (the Labour Association's Paper) and this became the real power for the movement that followed. Around the same time, he also established the Drammens Labour Association and the Christiania Labour Association. In 1850, the movement had 300,000 members and 300 local associations. Members included handicraft and industrial workers from towns, and 'husmenn' (like the people from Pasotorpet) and small farmers from rural areas. This rural response made the movement unique in Europe at that time. The thranitt's programme is often linked to the presentation of a 13,000-signature petition to the king on 19 May 1850. This petition demanded that everyone have the right to vote, that the public school system (where the rich traditionally came before the poor) be reformed, and that improvements be made to the harsh conditions experienced by the 'husmenn'.

The authorities did not leave Thrane or his organisation in peace. He received a prison sentence for 'blasphemous talk of God', even though the High Court had found him not guilty. On 7 July 1851, Thrane and a number of his associates were arrested and 127 men were subsequently imprisoned. Thrane received four years with hard labour.

The movement died with their imprisonment, and did not reappear until around the start of the twentieth century.

Finally released in 1858, Thrane travelled around Norway working as a photographer. The authorities dogged his footsteps, to ensure he did not restart the movement. In 1863, he fled to the United States, effectively becoming Norway's first political refugee. There he made a living from writing and photography, and was in demand as a lecturer. In 1890, he died in impoverished circumstances, in the United States. His body was returned to Norway and buried in Æreslunden (the Grove of Honour) at Vår Frelsers Church, Oslo, the city of his birth. The Norwegian Labour party gained power many years later, but Thrane's contribution is not forgotten. He is recalled whenever the Labour party (Arbeiderpartiet) celebrates, and at election time.

The reader may ask what an early labour leader such as Thrane has to do with migration to New Zealand, but I found his revolutionary ideas had reached its shores. Jack Curtis, a fourth generation New Zealander living in Manawatu, is very proud of his blood ties to Marcus Thrane, and has faded letters and papers to prove this relationship. Curtis believes Norway's proletariat was familiar with his ideas and, of course, concepts of social justice were able to take root much more easily in New Zealand than in Norway.

'I quite agree with you, Captain Nordby. Respect is so important.' He should have stopped there. He knew it. He was on thin ice, but could not help himself. However, the devil in him urged him to explore this theme.

'But respect applies to us all, don't you think? High or low, we all have to show respect. Respect each other I mean. My great teacher, Marcus Thrane, taught me that.'

Captain Nordby had some difficulties with the third glass. It came down on the mahogany table rather hard and lost some of its contents.

'Who? Marcus . . . that agitator . . .'

'. . . far-seeing . . . visionary . . .'

'. . . dead and buried, like Julius Caesar . . .'

'. . . ideas . . . alive and blossoming . . .'

'. . . utter nonsense . . . society to be protected . . .'

'. . . 13,000 signatures to the king . . .'

'. . . 13,000 idiots!'

The conversation had got out of hand. Elliot was quite ashamed of himself. He had lost his temper, lost his head, against all Christian's advice. And all because of the word 'respect', which had so many meanings. Too late to apologise or to start again.

The glass broke in the captain's hand. Of course he should have turfed this upstart out straightaway, this agitator of a landlubber. Now it was too late, the scoundrel had fled. He'd had the audacity to slam Nordby's cabin door as well.

Now, though, the captain's poor hand needed attention. There could well be splinters of glass in it for Doctor Mogstad to extract.

It was almost 24 hours before the captain appeared in the wheelhouse. Even then he tried to keep his bandaged hand inside his jacket.

Two weeks later, just north of the Cape Verde Islands, death boarded the ship as an unwanted passenger. This feared guest remained with them until the end of the voyage. Elliot had not met the captain since their encounter in the cabin, and he still felt badly about it. However, the first funeral was about to take place and Elliot considered it his simple duty to attend, at least for the sake of the passengers who had placed such trust in him.

The twins, Hans and Johan, were undernourished and weak even before they boarded the ship. The ship's doctor failed to notice this when he attempted to look them in the eyes. Nor had he noticed it when he glanced at their little hands as the frightened parents, each carrying a tightly wrapped baby, had passed by

Several unfortunate circumstances had caused the babies' health to deteriorate. The young parents, with a daughter three years older than the twins, understood *Høvding* was to sail in June. They were from Modum, by Tyrifjorden, an area where Marcus Thrane, the former labour leader, had been a teacher in the mid-1840s. Accordingly, the family farewelled Modum in mid-May and had covered twice the distance travelled by the Odalen people. Of course, when they reached Christiania, there was no *Høvding* to be seen. They received help from the Mission, but three months with little food and no money severely weakened all five of them.

The babies fared the worst. Their mother had no milk for them, and whatever liquid they were given was soon vomited back up. Nearly 6 months old, the twins died within hours of each other. The small family from Modum had no relatives aboard. Those who congregated on the aft deck to support the weeping parents, and to see the little ones to their grave, were mainly neighbours from the family section.

The mourners watched as the two sawhorses were put in place, one behind the other. Then came the wide plank with the polished surface, which jutted out at least a metre beyond the railing. A box containing earth, from shipowner Bull's farm at Nøtterøy, near Tønsberg, had also been produced. The box was an essential part of the ceremony, as three handfuls of soil would accompany the dead infants to their graves. All Mr Bull's ships carried the same funeral equipment, as death at sea was common.

Everything the captain required for the ceremony was now in place, apart from his Bible and book of hymns. These he brought himself from the locked sea chest in his cabin. Captain Nordby was in full uniform for this sad occasion, complete with his gold-trimmed hat with its shiny brim. A picture of quiet dignity and elegance.

Johanna, Christian and Fredrik wore their Sunday best – dark church clothes that hardly showed any mending. Even so, the men felt a little awkward without their hats. Johanna did not stand out amongst the other women mourners. She wore Randi's long black shawl, tightly wrapped around her body, a clean white blouse, last worn for her confirmation, and a small black shawl over her head that looked more like a large kerchief.

Elliot, too, was in his very best attire. He piously doffed his dark hat when second mate Olassen came across the deck with the grief-stricken parents and their little daughter. Olassen carried the twins, who were inside a shiny white canvas bag, which the ship's sail maker had just stitched up. It was the mother's wish that the infants should not be separated, even in death. Olassen carefully, ever so carefully, placed the canvas parcel onto the smooth plank, ensuring that the lead weights were closest to the railings. It was customary for corpses buried at sea to go to their graves feet first. He then respectfully removed his cap.

Captain Nordby did everything according to the book. The ceremony was correct, handled with decorum and dignity, and was in the right sequence. He had noticed Elliot Greiner among the mourners. No doubt, he was there solely to look for mistakes during the ceremony, so he could pick another quarrel. Not another glance did he cast in Greiner's direction.

At a signal, the mainsail on the main mast was lowered, the ship was straightened – and lost speed immediately. The captain removed his hat as a sign of respect and handed it to Olassen. He then shook the hands of the grieving parents. First the weeping mother, and then the small, bent father, who looked hopelessly lost and forlorn. Elliot could see the lips moving, but the words were lost to the sea breeze. There must have been some talk about what to sing, as the hymnbook was opened, the bookmark fell on the deck, and the captain burst into song. He was halfway through the second verse before the others joined him, haltingly and with great diversity.

Elliot listened in utter astonishment. The man had a beautiful voice. A deep, resonant bass voice. Not self-conscious or awkward like most of the others, but loud, strong and rich, as if he had a whole church organ inside him. What an incredible difference from the voice he heard in the cabin the other day. The man had changed entirely. So mild looking, so concerned, so compassionate, and his face seemed so smooth. Did he possess human feelings after all?

The voice remained firm and clear through to the end of the fourth verse. Then came moments of near silence. Elliot became conscious of heavy canvas flapping in the wind, waves hitting against the side of the ship, women with bent heads sobbing softly, and white handkerchiefs were constantly in motion.

Perhaps they all shared the same thoughts. Will we be

here again? Who will be next? Will it be one of ours? Will it be my child?

Captain Nordby did not preach a sermon. He read slowly and clearly from the Bible, and the old message came alive. Eternal life, and Jesus going ahead to prepare a room in his father's heavenly mansion for the little twins. Then he bent down, three times, and placed, oh so slowly, three handfuls of Nøtterøy soil on the white canvas. A crewmember, bare-footed, blue loose shirt and tussled hair, lifted the end of the shiny plank. The canvas coffin began to slide, slowly for a start, then gathering speed. No one saw it fall, but everyone heard the soft splash and a deep sigh went through the gathering.

The mainsail was raised. The ceremony was over. The ship gathered speed again. Despite the sadness of the occasion, this was a beautiful day in the South Atlantic Ocean. The sun was warm and the wind light and steady. The Bible and hymnbook were closed. The captain tried once more to comfort the parents, but they seemed oblivious to him. He returned to his cabin and all the funeral equipment was whisked away.

The mother and the father – now with the little girl in his arms – remained intertwined and still like a statue for some time. The girl had buried her head in her hands, not wanting to see. Perhaps she did not fully understand. Perhaps she just wept because her parents were weeping. The statue broke apart eventually. The little family headed unsteadily, as if blinded by their own tears, towards the main hatch and the ladder. Before descending into the ship, they turned and stared once more out over the ship's wake. They appeared to be trying to pinpoint where the twins' grave may have been.

Johanna had taken it all in. She had soaked it up and stored it away in her heart. She had been with the mother in her grief, with the small child, with the tussle-haired seaman during the calm, cold performance of his duty. She accepted nature's contrast between deep tragedy on one hand and warm sunshine and sparkling blue ocean on the other. Grief and beauty existed side by side. She could see that in the captain, as well, good and bad lived together at the same time. Contrast was life itself, and not something to be resolved.

Elliot's inner eye was focused on the captain. Was he more than just a bully? He could sing like the archangel Gabriel. There was no doubt about that. Still, was there really a softer side to him? Was he just an actor enjoying the limelight, and being the centre of attention in a morbid way? Was it all just a ritual, a play, and had he just held centre stage for a moment?

Fredrik had stopped by the main hatch. He saw the three sad figures shuffling in his direction. Here they stood for some time, gazing at the endless churchyard. It would have been so much better if it had all happened at home. In consecrated soil beside Modum Church, with a headstone and name – and entries in the church register. They slowly disentangled themselves and climbed down to the next deck to return to their canvas abode with its stuffy air. His thoughts followed very much the same pattern as those of the poor parents. What would happen to the poor twins down there? Their souls had been released in death. That he knew. They would be on their way to the Almighty. However, the bodies inside the white canvas? Would the lead weights take them to the bottom of the ocean? Was it dark there? He shuddered. Or would they simply sail around in the cold, wet darkness until the canvas rotted, perhaps to be eaten by fish in the end. He felt sick. Still, was it so much worse to be eaten by fish in the sea than by worms in the cemetery?

Perhaps the death of the twins was a sign to them all. Perhaps it meant that they were all to end that way. That they would never reach the Promised Land. He had heard of howling gales and huge waves that could break down even the strongest ships. This could happen to *Høvding* too.

In his heart of hearts, Fredrik had feared this journey. Thanks to good weather, and they had been fortunate so far, his fear had subsided. He had almost forgotten that nagging feeling. Today, though, it had flared up again, and to such an extent that, surely, everyone could see it in his face. The howling storm was sure to come eventually, with huge waves as high as the barn at Skara farm. Perhaps even higher. And they would break over the ship, break the three masts, break down the ship and . . .

The nausea he felt was not the nausea of the seasickness he encountered and conquered during the first days in the North Sea. No, this was the nausea of fear. Sheer cold fear.

A long time passed before the storm Fredrik had expected, finally hit. It was mid-October, and they were south of the Cape of Good Hope. By that time there had been eight more burial services. Each was for a small child and each time, as its little body twisted and turned its way into the dark depths, the ship's doctor had recorded in his journal: 'Cause of Death: Dysentery'. Ten children died within weeks, yet *Høvding* was still only halfway to its destination.

The ceremonies remained the same, with one exception. The tussle-haired seaman in the loose fitting blue shirt did not reappear after the burial of the twins. The ship's carpenter, a middle-aged man with greyish hair, a wind-hardened face, and eyes like the smiling Atlantic, took his place. All funeral equipment came from his workshop, so he was the obvious person to take part in the ritual. It was said that the seaman with the unruly hair had not been seen on deck for two days after the first funeral.

Near panic broke out among the mothers of young children after the fifth death. The men were fuming. They were just off Recife, in Brazil, on the point of turning southeast to pick up the favourable trade wind. Clearly, there was something horribly wrong aboard *Høvding* for so many to have died. There was no doubt either, as to whose fault it was. Captain Nordby's! He rationed the food, he rationed the water, he rationed everything, and it was all such poor quality anyway. He starved the little ones to death! Mothers wept and men swore, but to no avail.

Deputations and meetings with Olassen achieved nothing. The captain was, of course, beyond reach. Suggestions were offered and schemes formulated. Could they have some lemon juice, please? It was stated that it would be made available in the tropics. At least some for the children, please?

Could potatoes – please – white flour and some fresher type of food be brought to the galley just for the children? Only for the small ones! Mothers would prepare a special meal for them first thing every morning.

No! The answer was always no. Olassen pleaded and, no doubt, did his best. But the captain was adamant and his word was law. No, there would be no special this and special that. No exceptions, no favouritism. He disliked favouritism. The food was nourishing and good enough for everyone. Here the ship's doctor, his good friend, gave him full support. The daily wholesome rations would be brought to the galley at 6 a. m. each day as usual, and then the mothers could prepare the meals the way they wanted. That's that. Finished!

But – but – didn't the captain know that toddlers could not manage salt meat, mouldy bread and ship's biscuits that were as hard as Odalen rocks? Not week in and week out! Didn't he know when they brought it all up or could not swallow the smelly water, that it was a danger sign? From then on the child would deteriorate very quickly. Didn't he know that either? Or perhaps he would care to come down to the passengers' quarters and have a look for himself?

No, the captain did not care for that. Nor did he care for the constant complaints about food. Did the passengers not have something else to do? No games to play? No psalms to sing?

Yes, it was true the crew had slightly different fare, prepared in the crew's galley. They were workers. Dangerous and heavy work it was too, their strength had to be kept up. Heaven forbid if they fell sick, everything depended on them. Everyone's safety was at stake here. He had the highest regard for his crew from Tønsberg.

Perhaps Olassen would be kind enough to pass on one more point from the captain. He knew perfectly well that many passengers had brought their own provisions. Tidbits of all sorts. Since they were so obsessed with food, perhaps it was time they opened their own larders? Perhaps they could share some of their own goodies with their neighbours? Had they not heard about Jesus, who set such a good example for us all? Had they not heard about the two fishes and the five loaves? A little Christian charity would not go amiss.

Randi watched her little Julius like a hawk, especially after the twins died. The Pasotorpet larder had been opened immediately, and she thanked God for the dried rye bread and the smoked meat. Such wonderful little extras for the whole family. There was no doubt, though, that for the angel Julius, goat's milk cheese proved best of all.

It was when the ninth death occurred, Johanna later realised, that the breakthrough came. Meetings, delegations and conferences had achieved nothing. Elliot's form of diplomacy and plans made by Christian and some others bore no fruit at all it seemed. So the women took over, the seventy-eight mothers, and Johanna. Together, they attended the funeral of the ninth child at the stern.

Keep out of sight, was the order given to the men. Look after the children. Stay below deck. There on the aft deck the women stood, in their sombre shawls and mournful attire, forming a double line for the captain to pass between. Heads not bent low in sorrow as in the past, but doleful faces that stared accusingly at him. Not a word was said. Not a note was sung by the figures encased in black. Just the saddest of looks and the air of deepest tragedy. Captain Nordby went through the ritual without faltering, and appeared to be oblivious to the silent misery surrounding him. Something must have affected him though. He had no difficulty sweeping aside pleas, demands and threats from men, and loathed Elliot. However, these women, these eyes, these faces . . .

Next morning Olassen made it known that a new arrangement was to start. A young woman, a spinster, had been hired to prepare food for the babies each morning between 10 a. m. and 12 noon. Mothers could collect their rations from the galley. Who was the spinster who had been thrust into this responsible position? To prepare the food and then also to distribute it? A very important job indeed. Who could it be? It was Josephine. Josephine from Christiania, who was known for her loud laughter and provocative ways, her white teeth and her quick repartee.

Josephine was the secret centre of Fredrik's imaginary love life. She was very much in his thoughts, day and night. Silently and disturbingly . . . He became aware of her on the first day aboard ship. She had dropped her handkerchief and he had picked it up. The smile and the lively look she gave him had gone straight to his heart. And it had stayed there. She had lovely arms, softly rounded, and wonderful to touch for sure – and to stroke gently. Josephine's peals of laughter could be heard on deck many times a day. They held you, called you to attention better than church bells, and made you go closer to see what the laughter was about. Often the laughter didn't seem to be about anything. She also had a wonderful way of walking. Short mincing steps, and hips moving in such a cheerful manner.

Fredrik had also noticed her shapely white breasts, which attempted to burst their way out of her tight blouse. The remainder of her body, mysterious and hidden beneath that wide, ankle-length skirt, was the source of more than one restless fantasy during the voyage, as he lay in his bunk.

He had harboured sinful thoughts. There was no doubt

of that. In his mind, he had played with her white breasts, licked them, and even bitten them. He had explored her soft body with one hand – with both hands. 'Thou shalt not commit adultery.' Oh, he knew that. He knew that very well. He had been confirmed. The Lutheran catechism spelt it out very clearly, '. . . not commit adultery in thoughts, words or acts'. Acts, he was free from sin there. Not once had he committed carnal sin. Words, no again; he did not talk about his fantasies. Not to a living soul, heaven forbid. And he did not swear or use foul language – hardly ever. It was in his thoughts that he had fallen so deeply into sin, and now he was tortured twice over. Firstly, by sweet and unseemly fantasies, and secondly, by the knowledge of sinning.

True, a slightly better balance had been achieved lately. Even Fredrik had become aware that Josephine's language was a trifle coarse at times, and her voice a little on the loud side – and possibly heard too often. The scales, though, had been tipped by a comment she made to her friend Ellen the other morning, as they walked through the single men's quarters on their way to the ladder.

'Pooh! There's a smell of old billy goats here.' It was a cruel remark, and deeply hurtful to Fredrik. He now tried hard to dislike Josephine.

The mothers were delighted with the new arrangement, although they could have hoped for a more stable and competent person to be in charge. Josephine was the boss, but she had the good sense to accept assistance in the galley and there was no shortage of helping hands. The mothers were simply falling over each other in their eagerness to assist. Fresh bread appeared, almost white and baked the same morning. Meat was on the menu, obtained from large, hermetically sealed tins. And potatoes, blessed potatoes. Even puddings were dished up. The mothers were ecstatic. Josephine had not been popular among the women, but her star rose quickly now. It was believed she had good connections aboard.

5 The promised land

JOSEPHINE's popularity was short-lived. The wonderful supplies from the aft storeroom soon dried up, with the near-white bread being the first to go.

'Supplies not coming through,' she would say. 'I can only cook or bake with what I'm given, can't I?' She did not look people in the eye when she said that though. Liars have shifty eyes, and usually Josephine had no difficulty with eye contact. Did she steal? Did she take the food out of the mouths of the babies?

The women agreed, Josephine was just a brazen hussy. She'd always been like that. Now the hussy was pinching the babies' food as well.

Still, the mothers would soon have something else to think about.

The first sign of the storm was the appearance of white-capped waves far to the south on *Høvding*'s starboard side. The sea appeared dangerously dark in that direction. Next the spars creaked, the stays tightened, and the ship heeled over. The first mate's voice, almost as strong as the captain's, rang with urgency and authority. Canvas was shortened, and the foresail, mainsail and mizzen staysail were all lowered together. Fredrick found it unbelievable that things could happen so quickly, that the crew could work with such speed and precision.

The dark blue overtook and surrounded them. White tops frothed, like the mouths of wolves. Glistening white teeth gave chase and snapped at their heels. Suddenly, the few puffs of wind of only minutes earlier were incredibly strong, the strongest wind Fredrik had ever encountered. Salt spray covered his face and stung his eyes. *Høvding* listed sharply, yielding to the power that had borne down upon it. The first few waves tore at the railing, and then washed along the deck.

The few hardy passengers still on deck – albeit clinging like grim death to the railing – were ordered below. All young men, and all drenched to the skin, they had been frightened, yet fascinated at the same time.

Then came the dreaded order: 'Batten down the main hatch!'

The next few waves washed almost the full length of the ship. A huge wave tore at the crew before they could fully secure the hatch cover, and then cascaded down to the next deck – to the passengers' quarters. The ship rolled, then rose, then dived. The sea water amongst the emigrants on the lower deck washed from side to side, then rushed back, then forward. Within minutes, everything around them was soaked through.

It was difficult to find one's own belongings in the total darkness, let alone rescue them from the surging water and attempt to place them at a higher level. Soon there was total chaos below, and utter, utter, black misery.

Fredrik had sought out the illusion of personal security his bunk provided. There he held on with both hands and with all his might. Even so, he was thrown hard against the bulkhead when the ship rolled in one direction, and was in danger of being tossed out when the ship rolled in the other.

The seesawing motion continued at the same time it seemed, with *Høvding* seemingly plunging down into very deep valleys, then shuddering, righting itself for a moment, before climbing out. Fredrik felt his blood, his whole body-weight, rush to his head. Next moment, after the corresponding draining feeling in his stomach, he was almost standing in his bunk. And, of course, everything in his body now surged back towards his feet. He felt sick. No! More than that. He felt desperately ill. The urge to vomit overwhelmed him, but where could he do that?

That the sea would take him had always been Fredrik's greatest fear. Now here he was, trapped in total darkness between two decks, with the sea trying to break in. *Høvding* was being pounded to bits, he imagined, and their endless journey into the cold depths would soon begin. Not just him, but also the hundreds of other stiff bodies.

Fredrik wanted to fold his hands and pray, but did not dare release the sides of his bunk. Even so, he managed to plead with the Almighty with all his heart. Could he be forgiven for all his sinful thoughts over many weeks? He desperately hoped for a sign that God had heard his prayer and would admit his soul to the Heavenly Kingdom.

Others, too, were convinced their last hour was at hand. And these were long hours – as the storm raged for almost two days. The passengers had been fortunate until this time, and had not previously encountered any bad weather to speak of. However, once south of the Cape of Good Hope, things had changed abruptly. They were now experiencing King Neptune's fury.

Sighs, shouts, shrieks, prayers and urgings for forgiveness emitted from all quarters within the middle deck. The raging storm and the creaking timbers deafened all other sounds. Human voices were like faint whispering. The extreme pangs of seasickness were not Fredrik's alone. The stench of vomit and excreta now filled the space and became worse with every hour.

Some who thought their death was nigh turned apathetic. They were hardly conscious of their evil-smelling world, and only longed to be set free. Prayers were mumbled between closed lips. Please God, let it happen quickly.

It took those people a long time, even after they had opened their eyes, to recognise grey daylight seeping in. The hatch cover had been removed. The storm was over, or almost over. And the danger at least had passed.

Høvding still dived into dark valleys and reared up like a stallion. Its three towering masts swung in great arcs against the sky. Grey clouds – all torn and patched – scurried overhead, but the wind was dying down. The sea remained a frightening sight, a wilderness in black and white. Its deepest darkest valleys still had snowy mountains that hissed and foamed on top.

The mizzen staysail was set, and the royals were unfurled a moment later. The ship steadied itself a little, and then responded more obediently to the helmsman's efforts. Next it flew forward like a wounded bird before the wind, and began weaving in and out of black valleys that still bore an ominous resemblance to gaping jaws.

Trembling people, still unusually unsteady on their feet, began appearing on deck. They needed to clear their lungs with badly needed fresh air, before facing the daunting task of cleaning up below. Many fell on their knees, without sense of embarrassment, and thanked God for their deliverance.

Fredrik was amongst the first to crawl up the ladder when the hatch cover was removed. His senses were opened as never before. God had not only forgiven him, he had also given him a new life. The sea air, which had whipped the foam from atop the waves, tasted wonderfully of salt. He could taste, he could hear, he could see! Sails filled and billowed, then fell back and slapped against the spars between gusts.

The crew were all around him, some laughing, some swearing, some replacing tattered sails, mending the rails on the port side, or repairing the slight damage to the wheelhouse. Again, they worked quickly and efficiently, and they all seemed to be there. The three mates also, as well as the ship's carpenter. And the elderly sail maker. He had bundled up all the torn canvas and taken it to his workshop under the fo'c'sle. It was all action and life. Life! None had the fear of death in his eyes.

'It could have been worse.' Olassen walked past, giving Fredrik a smile. He must have been right, as before the day was over, there was no damage to be seen, neither on deck nor aloft.

However, things were different on the passenger deck. There chaos reigned. All bedding, saturated with sea water and the rest, had to be taken up on deck, to eventually be washed and dried. That was the easier part. The worst was the cleaning up – with buckets, shovels, mops and brooms. The buckets did not fill themselves, nor did they reach the railing unaided, to be emptied over the side. This unpleasant task mostly fell to the single men and women. Even Josephine was seen to lend a hand and become part of the bucket chain.

When Fredrik descended the ladder to play his part in this Herculean task, he was almost driven back by the indescribable stench. He could not imagine how people had survived so long in that hellish hole. The small children, for the most part, seemed to have coped better than their parents. Some appeared now, though, after the ordeal, to be very tired. They just wanted to sleep. And among these was little Julius.

Randi was concerned. Should she try to give him some food at this stage? There was a little blueberry juice left in her box, or perhaps blackcurrant from Kuggerud Farm might be better? However, she let him sleep on. He would wake up by himself soon enough. Randi sat in silence. People continued working all around her. Full daylight came in through the hatch, which was now wide open, and the air seemed less foul. Randi also felt strangely limp.

Julius was not well. Randi placed her hand on his forehead, and checked with her lips as well. The child seemed a little hotter each time, and tiny beads of perspiration had appeared. Please God, don't, don't let it happen to my little Julius . . .

Johanna had some difficulty finding Christian. Finally, though, there he was on deck, the last man in the bucket chain, tipping his fifteenth load of saltwater slop over the side of the ship. He saw instantly that something was wrong. Her eyes had betrayed the situation.

'Yes, it is Julius. No, not dead. But he is behaving like all the others before they died. Olassen please, can you bring him down, straightaway? Mama is so alarmed.'

They found Randi seated on a bundle of tarpaulins on her dampish mattress. She held Julius tightly to her body with one arm. A spoon was in her hand. Three daughters surrounded her, staring with big frightened eyes. Johan, too, just stood there feeling helpless. Julius was deadly pale. His head hung to one side as if the strength had gone from his body.

'He won't take anything. It all comes back up again.' She had tried juice, she had tried water mixed with sugar. She had even tried a spoonful of real milk from a nursing mother, bless her. Nothing helped. It all came up again as soon as he tried to swallow. And, what's more, he had diarrhoea.

'You must get the doctor, you simply must.' She looked pleadingly at both Christian and Olassen, and desperation was not far away. She had been through so much in the last forty-eight hours. Doctor Mogstad did appear. Unwillingly. This was very much against his principles. The air was foul down there too. What odours! Definitely unhealthy. How could people live in such squalor?

Dysentery was the verdict after a brief examination of the patient. 'Try a little sugar water with a pinch of salt.'

'Salt? Does the doctor think . . .' Yes, the doctor thought so. That was all he could recommend to Randi under the circumstances.

Julius did not take kindly to the new medicine. He vomited yet again. Tears began running down Randi's cheeks as she wept silently. Her daughters and then her husband, in fact the whole Paso family cried with her. All cried more or less noiselessly, their little canvas alcove having become as cheerful as a morgue.

Christian had not shown Doctor Mogstad back to the ladder. Nor did he take further part in the hectic cleaning-up campaign. He just watched his future in-laws in their grieving and their utter misery.

'Oh God, let me think of something. Let me be helpful.' His prayers must have been answered, for within moments he was by his own bunk fishing the remaining few shillings he possessed from under his pillow. Olassen could still be helpful.

He found the second mate without difficulty, hovering by the wheelhouse as usual. Olassen seemed to be there most of the time, whether it was his watch or not. Thank God. He understood the request immediately, even if it was unusual.

'Port wine, any sort of port? Well, it cannot do any harm. It's a well-known medicine for adults anyway, and it has a calming effect. Hmm, might come in very useful. If not for the baby, then perhaps for the parents.'

Randi sat where Christian had left her. Julius, deadly pale and as limp as a rag doll, was still in her arms and the spoon was still in her hand.

'Port, try a spoonful of that!'

Miracle of all miracles: Julius swallowed. He licked his lips too. He wanted more! The port wine did not come back up.

Randi cried once more, but this time with relief. 'Oh, thank God. I was so scared.' The girls laughed and Johan smiled – and Johanna did something she had never done before in the presence of her parents. She threw her arms around Christian and kissed him.

'Oh, our hero, my darling! You have saved my baby brother!'

Christian may have thought it a little early to be given hero status, but he rejoiced in the warm feeling that now engulfed him. He had been thrust into the very centre of the Paso clan. A son-in-law that Randi could rely on. Everyone's pillar of support, a trusted helper, a . . . And Johanna loved him.

Christian's hero status did not diminish over the next few days. Far from it. Julius had no difficulty taking his spoonfuls of port, and was soon able to enjoy small goodies from the Paso food box. He improved visibly day by day. The good news spread like wildfire amongst the mothers. Others were also able to find a few shillings at the bottom of their bags or chests – and headed off to find Olassen and his wonder medicine. A hero's halo shone over Christian's head.

Høvding was now at its halfway point. There was only one more death to come, while five births were to occur before they reached their destination.

They were now heading due east in the Indian Ocean, and with a steady following wind. The weather was balmy once more. The washing, cleaning and drying of bedding proved easier than expected. The emigrants often slept on the deck, as they had done in the Atlantic before the storm. Oh, the joy of getting away from their hot, stuffy and still smelly quarters, and to see the stars again at night. The stars seemed huge in the black sky. Even bigger than at Pasotorpet and certainly more of them. Why should that be? Christian wondered.

They saw shoals of flying fish – fins spread like wings – emerge from wave tops, skim long distances across the surface and then disappear into other waves. What a wonderful sight. Best, though, were the porpoises at play. Whole packs of them. They came from nowhere, frolicked by the stern for a moment, then shot forward in long leaps to play just ahead of *Høvding*, their sleek black bodies glistening in the blue. Christian and Johanna never tired of watching them whenever they stood, always close together, by the railing.

They are whales, Olassen had said, not fish. Fish or whales? It meant little to the man of the forest. They both lived in the sea, didn't they?

Wonder of all wonders – flying fish even appeared on deck! Each morning, twenty or thirty of them still flapping their tails. They went straight into the frying pan.

Why, though, did they only land there at night? On this subject, Christian was mystified.

The children's health improved. There was no doubt about that. Some thought it was due to 'Christian's Wonder Medicine', as it was now called. Others believed it was the lemon juice now being doled out more freely. The captain had become much more generous after they had passed the halfway point. Christian wondered if it was the flying fish, and if a small change in diet could have made such a big difference to their sense of well-being.

Looking back much later, the Paso people thought the three weeks spent crossing the Indian Ocean had been easily the best part of the voyage. The time was trouble free. The wind was steady, the days warm, the nights beautiful – and the food was adequate. When they drew level with Fremantle, albeit two days from land, the captain set a more southerly course. The ship listed to port. The wind also grew stronger and colder, even though they were heading towards summer.

'We may see Cape Leeuwin,' Olassen had said. 'But we'll go south of Tasmania, then straight for Stewart Island. That's part of Ny Seland,' he added when he saw Christian's puzzled face. Geography was not the passengers' strong point, but Christian understood the connection between Ny Seland and Stewart Island. Suddenly the Promised Land was close. They would be there soon.

Flying fish no longer appeared, they must have preferred warmer water. The porpoises remained, but were not as plentiful as before, nor as playful. Even so, Christian and Johanna still spent hours by the railing. A new, wonderful sight – the albatross – had appeared. These birds were huge. So much bigger than the woodgrouse and hawks of Odalen, or the raven or falcon – and their shape was very different. They could skim the water like the flying fish, yet never touch it. Their long thin wings must be enormously strong. How could they follow *Høvding*, wheel about and overtake it with ease, without even flapping their wings? How could they soar for hours and still regulate their speed? It was a great mystery to Christian, and Johanna could not help him.

It must have been around this time that a rumour sprang to life. A harmless little flame for a start, but one that spread like wildfire among the passengers.

The captain was often on deck after they were south of the Great Australian Bight. At times, when his mood suited, he even shared little jokes with the passengers. A typical conversation might be:

'How did you cope with the storm? Were you sick?'

'Oh yes. Sick as a dog.'

'Still you seem to be alive and well. It may be worse where you are going.'

'Does the captain mean . . .'

'I'm just thinking it may be better to die at sea than to be eaten by cannibals.'

'Cannibals?'

'People who eat people, you know. Ny Seland is full of them. We'll turn around and get away as soon as we can.'

The captain had been in a good humour.

The news of cannibalism and the gruesome fate that awaited the immigrants had reached Elliot Greiner in no time. This was going too far! To scare the passengers, to intimidate them, to lie, to . . . Action was needed. Letters of complaint should be written to both the New Zealand and

Norwegian Governments. Captain Nordby should be unmasked. He should stand trial if possible, and, above all else, he should be held responsible for the deaths of the babies.

It was the historian, Val Burr, of Palmerston North, who first showed me a copy of this letter. Later I found a copy in the Norsewood Pioneer Museum. Bror Erik Friberg, whom we met earlier in the book, had translated it into English. I believe the actual author was Friberg's German-born wife, Cecilia Elizabeth, using the long Gothic 'S'.

Høvding's long voyage ended in Napier on 1 December 1873, although today the harbour it reached is too shallow to accommodate ships. The town was largely razed on 3 February 1931 by a major earthquake, which is noted as one of New Zealand's worst disasters.

The earthquake and the resulting fire claimed 256 lives in the region, including 161 in Napier. Around 3600 hectares of land near Napier was thrust upwards. As a result, a new port was built and the old one became a marina for small boats. Even the city's airport, some 2 kilometres from the port, was until 1931, part of the seabed.

The very large-scale reconstruction work that followed – mostly using the architectural style in vogue at that time – has resulted in Napier becoming recognised internationally for its many Art Deco buildings.

Everyone was on deck when *Høvding* entered Napier Harbour and was manoeuvred to its anchorage off Ahuriri. It had been at sea for 110 days. Excitement was rife aboard ship. It seemed to Christian and Johanna that they had both been on deck for a whole week. The lookout had shouted, 'Land ahead!' This had signalled the appearance of Stewart Island, which they had rounded well to the south due to treacherous inshore islands. They now had land off the port side, which appeared to be bush-clad right down to the water's edge. Still, there was no sign of farming activity. Perhaps there are farms there, Christian thought, but small and hidden in the vast forest like Odalen.

The previous day, in the early morning light, they had seen a group of small islands, also on the port side.

Solander Islands, Olassen had said, named after a Swede who was here one hundred years ago. They looked naked, and so hard and lonely.

The sea appeared red one day. In fact, it was red as far as they could see. When a seaman threw a bucket on a rope over the side and pulled it up again, they saw the water was full of tiny creatures. They looked like the shrimps from Christiania Fiord, only smaller. Several hours later, the waves were blue once more.

Again, they were fortunate with the weather. Light winds blew from the south as they sailed the full length of the South Island. Once more, the land was on their port side. The air was extremely clear and in the distance, they could see an endless row of white peaks. The land below the mountains seemed yellow. Were there farms there? What would they grow? Christian pondered. Or did they simply farm animals? And where was the forest with the huge trees he had heard so much about?

Two peninsulas were clearly visible as they sailed by. One, which was high and knobby, Christian later discovered was called Banks Peninsula. The other one was long and low, and jutted far out to sea. Here the snow-capped mountains appeared almost to rise from the beach.

Cook Strait, Olassen said the next day. The sea was rough here, and they could not see the passage between the two islands.

What they saw ahead, though, greatly excited Christian. Finally, there were mountains. Green mountains. The Tararua Ranges! Decidedly lower than those further south and without snow. And they were green! Surely, that must be the forest with the big trees. Still, there would be more than that. The lighter green, all those lighter patches? Could that be farmland?

The air was no longer as clear as it had been earlier. Was it haze or was it smoke? Christian thought he could smell smoke. Could they be burning the forest – in there, far away? The cosy familiarity of wood-smoke brought back memories of Odalen.

Smoke from some early 'bush burn' might well have drifted offshore from Wairarapa, where other Scandinavians, including Norwegians from Odalen, had settled the previous year. Perhaps it came from as far as Manawatu, on the other side of the Tararua Ranges. There, even more of his country-men and women, who had arrived two years earlier – including folk from Odalen – were also busy clearing their land. It was sometimes possible, he had heard, to smell New Zealand long before seeing it. Still, this usually only happened when ships approached in the late summer bush burning season. Perhaps, though, the smells he sensed were simply wishful thinking.

Høvding edged closer to land. It passed high grey cliffs that looked smooth, sheer, and almost milky-white in places. There were beaches and open land too, but no sign of settlements or farms. The deep green chain of mountains stayed alongside them all day. They did not seem very high and had softly rounded hills.

Late in the afternoon they rounded a cape. The cliffs were still high and very steep, but were yellowish, with darker streaks that suggested trolls might have painted them. What strange rocks! A big bay was opening up to the east, while a long irregular headland was visible to the north. Perhaps it was another peninsula. The ship's canvas was shortened and the sails were lowered.

'We shall be there tomorrow,' Olassen remarked.

Be there. There! Their future home. Christian and Johanna succumbed to the excitement of this moment. Forgotten were the hardships, all the bad things, the never-ending struggle for food, for water, the storm, the deaths . . . Now it was just the two of them. Together they would conquer all future adversity.

It took longer than expected to get ashore at Napier. Everyone had to remain aboard until all health checks were complete, which took most of the day. It was not until late afternoon on 1 December 1873 that *Høvding* was manoeuvred against the wharf and the gangway was made fast.

Christian and Johanna were among the first immigrants whose 'sea legs' somewhat unsteadily carried them ashore. As they stood hand in hand on the wharf, their new land certainly seemed to move beneath them.

A Province in the Melting Pot

History

In the early 1870s, the peak period of immigration from Norway to New Zealand, New Zealand was divided into large semi-autonomous provinces. These included Hawke's Bay Province, which had been established in 1858. Invariably conflicts occurred between the Wellington-based central government, and the provincial councils, for whom self-interest and jealousy often predominated over things which might have been in the national interest. Thus, in 1876, the central government abolished the provincial councils. Naturally, this action was unpopular with those who favoured – or perhaps profited from – the provincial system of government. However, the trend in the 1870s was towards a centrally directed country and economy.

Following the demise of the provincial councils, the central government subdivided the rural areas into many comparatively small (and therefore less troublesome) counties. Each of these counties then had its own county council. Norsewood, for example, became part of Waipawa County.

The Vogel Scheme

Sir Julius Vogel's expansive (and expensive) policy, in vogue at that time, involved borrowing heavily overseas. This aimed to provide the means to open up New Zealand's interior and establish the young colony's economy. Vogel, as Minister of Finance (also Premier 1873-76), visited London in 1871 and again in 1874-75, to arrange loans for the scheme. The purpose of the scheme was to build roads, railways and telegraph lines – the country's communications infrastructure – and convert the dense forest found in some regions into farmland. This policy became known as the Vogel Immigration and Public Works Scheme.

Compared now to New Zealand's much criticised 'Think Big' policies of the 1970s, Vogel's scheme required a large labour force that could be induced to live in remote, inhospitable places. Such places offered little attraction to earlier settlers who were now established in more developed parts of the country. At least, they were not interested while the really hard work remained to be done.

Virtually no published literature existed on New Zealand at this time that non-English speaking immigrants could read. Such immigrants could not really assess what might lie ahead for them in New Zealand. This was especially a problem for those 'foreigners' with limited education. As a result, many who came struggled with a reality bearing little resemblance to the promises made by migration agents – or to the migrants' own silver-lined dreams. This situation especially applied to the earliest emigrants. It was these people whose letters home had the potential to make or break a fragile new migration chain.

It is noteworthy that the earliest small 'experimental' group that – unknowingly – had the all important role of initiating this emigration chain, came to the rather better-situated bush clearing that is now the city of Palmerston North. It is also thought that letters by disillusioned migrants stood somewhat less chance than did optimistic letters of actually reaching families back home in Scandinavia.

Such was the control that the New Zealand Government had, through its agents such as Friberg, over the fledgling settlements. These impoverished peasant-settlers were politically naïve, as well as physically and socially (due to language barriers and ethnocentricity) isolated from the wider community.

Throughout the 1870s, the New Zealand Government assisted some 100,000 people to migrate from Britain and Northern Europe, although assistance to the latter group ceased in 1876. Possibly no other ethnic group assisted at that time was more suited to bush clearance and heavy manual work than the Scandinavians. Of this grouping, the Norwegians – most being rural-dwellers and already familiar with bush work – became regarded by the New Zealand Government as the most preferred for this task.

The bush settlements

Six once-remote bush settlements in the Lower North Island are associated with Scandinavian migration to New Zealand. In 1871, a small group of Norwegians, Swedes and Danes from two ships, came to Manawatu, to become Palmerston North's first settler families. The following year, five ships brought Scandinavians for settlement at Mauriceville in Wairarapa, and at Dannevirke, Norsewood and Makaretu in Southern Hawke's Bay. In 1873, still more arrived including settlers for Mellemskov (now Eketahuna) in Northern Wairarapa.

Some shiploads were settled in other parts of the country, although in a less organised manner than occurred with these six bush settlements. Of these settlements, one is now a city. Another, Dannevirke, grew from being very much in the shadow of Norsewood, to become the main town in the Tararua District. Norsewood and Eketahuna are also in the Tararua District. Quite close to Norsewood, but in the Central Hawke's Bay District, is Makaretu. It is some distance from both the main road and the railway, but a bridle path created between Norsewood and Makaretu in the early 1890s reduced the distance the settlers in these places commuted to a mere 10 kilometres. The road it became is now closed. Mauriceville, in Wairarapa District, is also many kilometres from the main road, although the Wairarapa railway line still passes through.

The Norwegians stand out as the only Scandinavian migrants whose migration chain included many people from a specific rural district in their homeland. As a result, and because shiploads of passengers were not normally given a choice about where they would be settled, extended families became spread throughout New Zealand.

Norsewood's early population consisted of settlers from all three Scandinavian countries and Germany. The latter included

Danes from Schleswig-Holstein and ethnic Poles from Northern Germany, who did not necessarily identify with the Prussian state that now dominated their homelands.

The New Zealand Government had named Norsewood (and Dannevirke) before the Scandinavian emigrants arrived. This was intended to create a sense of Scandinavian identity with the town. Furthermore, nearby roads received the names Danish Line, Swedish Line and German Line, in acknowledgement of settlers from those groups. For various reasons, these are now respectively called the Norsewood-Ormondville Road, Third Line North and Te Whiti Road.

People of influence

There were three central characters involved with migration to, and the development of, the Hawke's Bay Province in the early 1870s. These were John Davies Ormond, the Provincial Superintendent, Dr Isaac Featherston, New Zealand's London-based Agent General in 1871, and Bror Erik Friberg, a Swedish immigrant.

A man of action

It seems unlikely the exodus from southeast Norway to New Zealand would have achieved anything like the 1872-75 figures without Friberg.

Born in Stockholm on 8 August 1839, Friberg was university-educated and had gained qualifications in forestry. In 1866 he was in the old *Freistadt* (Free State) of Lübeck, an independent, duty-free town. His German-born wife, Cecilia Elizabeth, was a trained nurse and midwife. The young couple appear to have been idealistic and altruistic, as well as having personal ambitions. They emigrated from Hamburg and, after initially living in Auckland, settled in Napier in 1868. A biography in preparation on the couple will in due course shed proper light on them and their lives.

When he learnt of the New Zealand Government's intentions,

Friberg wrote to Ormond, the Superintendent of the Hawke's Bay Province, and warmly recommended his own services.

In his letter of 7 October 1871, Friberg advised that he knew the Scandinavian temperament, he spoke a language understood by everyone, and was well-qualified for the job. He also felt confident he could bring the type of worker and settler the province needed. He claimed he could: *assist in the advancement of the colony, where I have worked for five years and made my permanent home . . . understand the requirements of the province . . . succeed in recruiting immigrants of good class . . . promising land and good conditions . . . suggesting free return travel and a daily allowance of 12 shillings (including) 10 shillings for every adult person recruited . . .*

At first Ormond was suspicious about employing a non-British subject for this task. After interviewing Friberg he changed his mind. The Swede was clearly both able and persuasive, and had the great advantage of being able to speak the language of the perspective immigrants.

Under crossfire

Even in its infancy, Vogel's immigration policy was not without critics. The *Evening Post* of 2 April 1872 (by which time Friberg was in Norway) undertook a vitriolic attack on Ormond and Dr Featherston. This not only targeted the policy, but also the two men themselves, each of whom received a taxpayer-funded daily allowance of 18 shillings. The *Evening Post* expressed shock at the waste of public money being spent on greedy opportunists.

Still, the most vehement attack was reserved for Friberg. He was described as a 'bought parasite', who could know little of the enormous resources of this fertile land. The article claimed Friberg was feathering his own nest from over-generous pocket money obtained from hard-pressed taxpayers.

Høvding reached Napier on 16 September 1872 with its first contingent of Norwegian immigrants. However, these people soon turned on Friberg. They had come from poverty and had again found poverty. Now they found themselves indebted to the New Zealand Government, both for their passages and for their 40-acre blocks of jungle. Furthermore, paid work was not as plentiful as had been anticipated. And there was no money for return tickets.

They now concluded they had been misled from the beginning – and they blamed Friberg for their misery.

A different letter

True, preparations to receive the 1872 settlers had not been good. Provisions were inadequate and the surveying of their blocks was incomplete. Friberg, in turn, blamed the Hawke's Bay Provincial Government for this dilemma, and with some justification.

Understandably, Friberg was apprehensive about this second batch of *Høvding* immigrants. Would they turn against him too? Preparations were better this time – and surveying was complete. Employment and food supplies, however, remained a problem. Still, there was little Friberg could do except apply pressure to the authorities.

Friberg had been appointed Government Officer in charge of Scandinavian Settlements, as well as postmaster at Norsewood. He was to live among his immigrants, and it was essential he had their confidence. He needed them to view him as being on their side.

Elliot Greiner's letter of complaint about *Høvding*'s captain played into Friberg's hands. This would enable him to show the immigrants he would protect their interests. The letter, written at sea on 1 December 1873, appears to have been translated by Friberg the same evening. It was handed to the Immigration authorities the next day.

The letter's aim was to bring Captain Nordby to court. The long, involved letter enumerates the captain's perceived sins and misdemeanors: *The contract states that we should have good, wholesome food, instead . . . The captain should listen to . . . Entitled to juice in the tropics . . . Responsible for many deaths . . . Special food for babies in the hands of an irresponsible person . . . Sunday church meetings not held in spite of . . .* The letter, which ends with Second Mate Olassen being warmly recommended for future higher offices, was signed: *Your obedient servant, Elliot Greiner, on behalf of 78 families, spinsters and bachelors.*

Captain Nordby was not brought to court, despite Friberg's efforts. The reason given was that there was no proper evidence against him.

Thus, Bror Erik Friberg was unsuccessful in his attempt to gain the full confidence of these immigrants. He died, disappointed and disillusioned, on 3 February 1878, at the age of 38. He is buried at Norsewood Cemetery, surrounded by his immigrants and their families.

Doubtless, by the time they joined him, the vast majority of these immigrants had concluded that in the end, they had made the right choice in agreeing to follow him. Certainly, when Cecilia Friberg died in 1913, four former passengers from the 1872 voyage (E. O. Olsen, O. O. Nordbye, O. Lund and C. E. Pettersen) honoured her and her husband by carrying her coffin to its last resting place.

It is noteworthy, though, that as late as 1892, hundreds of Hawke's Bay's assisted immigrants, including Johanna's family and that of Elliot Greiner, had still not repaid their passage money to the New Zealand Government.* Probably most of these people never did.

---

* *Appendices to the Journals of the House of Representatives*, 1892, D-3A, page 5.

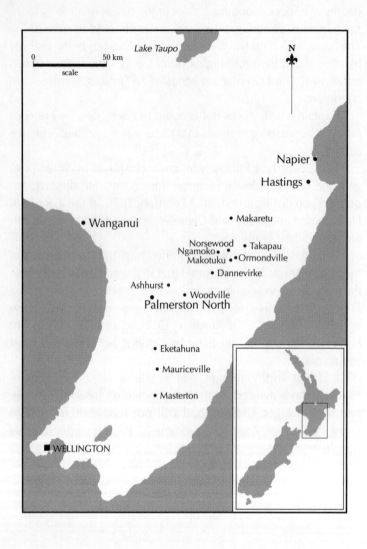

'Timber for house-building is free; growing on your own plot of land,' said the agent Bror Erik Friberg.

Part Two
Struggles in the Bush

6 The first Christmas

Today, when you travel from Palmerston North to Napier, you first drive through flat farmland and market gardens. You then enter the deep and spectacular Manawatu Gorge, which could just as easily be a piece of Norway.

At the other end of the gorge, you enter what was once called the 'Seventy-Mile-Bush'. So, where is the bush today? It's just about all gone. Admittedly, as you travel you see trees. However, they are not the primeval forest of the 1870s. They are either heavy, shapeless, sombre-looking macrocarpa trees, the small clusters of which remind one of groups of brooding trolls. Or they are dark pine trees, seemingly marching in straight lines like obedient soldiers, and not in the least like the tall slender, red-barked pine trees we know from Norway.

Still, pockets of bush do remain in gullies and creek beds. And, thank goodness, there is one sizeable reserve, at Ballance, at the eastern mouth of the Manawatu Gorge. Here, ancient bush dating to Gondwana and the time before the continents separated is so dense the sky is scarcely visible to those who explore its carefully prepared walkways.

Here you find the giant rimu, once a slender, softly curving and feminine-looking seedling. Also the liana, the tawa, the tall, wet-footed kahikatea, and at least one totara that must be hundreds of years old.

Christian rose slowly and wiped the sweat from his brow. He had struggled with this obstinate stump all day. It was essential that it be moved, as this was the house site. He had started clearing the bush from his land, but it seemed a near invisible start.

True, Johanna's uncle, Christoffer Finnsen had said in his letter that trees must be cleared away before the wonderfully fertile soil beneath them could be used. Surely, it was fertile? Otherwise, how could it support growth like this?

Not in his wildest dreams, though, had Christian imagined the forest might be like this. So dense, so dark, and blocking out the sunlight. It was green, many shades of green, that was true, but still only one colour. And no flowers, nothing that could lift or give a sparkle to the bush scene. It was all rather dreary, especially as he was there alone. Still, one thing cheered him in this green wilderness. A little moss-green bird that twittered and sang like an angel. It was amazing how many sweet notes its little throat could produce. Did he destroy its home by cutting down the trees? Those trees that depressed him so much.

Christian felt somewhat ashamed to find himself thinking like that. Still, the thoughts kept cropping up, no matter how hard he tried to banish them from his mind. He also felt small and uneasy in the semi-darkness below the towering trees. Ferns and supplejacks slowed him further and held him back. Did they want to strangle him, or to push him away perhaps, before he started the attack in earnest? Could he win this battle on his own? Or would it be a lifetime's work to clear it all away, before he would have the paddocks, stock and house he had promised Johanna?

Yes, Johanna. His heart ached. He had not seen her since

he left Napier with the other men nearly three weeks ago. How is she getting on? Has she settled in well with the Cornford family? Are they looking after her? Being kind to her, and teaching her English as they promised? How does Johanna like her work as a domestic servant? And does she miss me as much as I miss her? Oh, an impossibility!

Only three more days. Then on Thursday morning at daybreak, he would set off for Napier.

Christian had paid employment now, three days on and three days off; doing road construction work like most of the other new settlers. They were divided into two gangs: Monday to Wednesday and Thursday to Saturday. Then they swapped days every two weeks. The free time was intended to allow the immigrants to work on their own land. There was one major drawback of course – the New Zealand forest had turned out to be a stubborn enemy.

If he walked fast, unencumbered by baggage, could he do it in two days? And by sleeping at Waipawa? He smiled. There was so much to tell Johanna. The house site was almost cleared. Other trees had been felled as well, and they could plant potatoes around the roots of the felled trees. Settlers who had arrived the previous year assured him it was not too late to plant potatoes just after Christmas. They would mature in three months and could be dug before the frosts came. It upset him that he had bad news as well. He now knew it would take him much longer than he had expected to clear his land. This could mean he would be dependent on paid labouring work for many years to come. It was all so very different from the rich fields and fat cattle they had imagined for their future while still at Pasotorpet and at sea.

Christian had eight days break from the roadwork over Christmas, so there was plenty of time to discuss future plans with Johanna. But where could he stay in Napier?

'Yes, Ma'am!' Johanna had learnt her first words of English, and she enjoyed using them.

She had been very apprehensive the day she came to the big white house on the outskirts of Napier. It looked so grand and overpowering. She felt small and out of place, but it did not take long to understand there was nothing to be scared of. Mrs Cornford was a lovely person. Warm and understanding, full of smiles and laughter and – just as important – she was only ten years older than Johanna herself. In spite of language problems, the pair quickly established a good rapport. The same situation applied to the two girls, Jessica, aged 6, and Christina, aged 4. The children were curious about the new servant girl, with her strange clothes and even stranger language. They were all smiles and big round eyes. Johanna smiled back. Soon two-way trust was established and 'Auntie Johanna' became part of the household.

Johanna had her own room, her own dresser, and her very own wardrobe. What unheard-of luxury! Her two heavy skirts from Pasotorpet, her blouses and her black shawl were packed away. The dress she wore was a gift from Mrs Cornford. 'No,' she had said, 'too small and tight for me. I simply cannot wear it any longer. I have been looking for someone to use it. Oh yes, you would do me a favour. It suits you so well too.'

There was a mirror above the dresser in her room. Johanna paid many visits there over the next few days, her heart pounding. How would Christian like her new dress? Would he find it too short, too tight, or a little frivolous perhaps? She wore an apron most of the time, a long apron with short sleeves. Her beautiful new dress must stay clean as long as possible.

Six-year-old Jessica became Johanna's main language teacher. When their mother was out, and that happened often, it was Johanna's job to care for the two little girls. They would sit at the big table in the dining room, with sheets of paper, pencils and crayons spread before them.

A clock, a cat, a picture, wall, floor, ceiling – and so on.

Jessica supplied the words as Johanna pointed to them. Then she wrote the sounds down as phonetically as her alphabet would allow. Domestic objects were soon mastered. Then came numbers, colours and personal pronouns. What fun it was to learn something new and useful! Johanna learnt quickly too. It was no coincidence that she had stood closest to the altar at her confirmation in Grue Church. Jessica was an eager teacher, full of words and explanations. Christina helped as well, but most of the time, she sat gazing at the strange pupil, eyes as big as saucers and fingers in her mouth.

'Yes Ma'am? I am coming.' Johanna stood up from the big table, leaving her two charges behind. She felt proud of herself for being able to respond promptly to Mrs Cornford's call from the kitchen, and with the right tone of voice. She wanted to convey willingness as well as respect. Happy to be of service! Justly so. That's why she was paid a shilling a day. On top of that, she received food and clothing, and had her own room. Never, never in all her life had she felt so well, so rich, and so happy to exist. At least her own existence – for dark clouds loomed regarding so much else.

Was it money that had raised her self-esteem? Johanna received her wages every Friday, and already there were 12 shillings in the drawer below her mirror. Two more weeks and she'd have more than one New Zealand pound. The money would come in very handy when she and Christian set up house together; and that day might not be far off. Had Christian obtained his block of land as promised? Was it nice and flat? Could they buy their first cow straightaway? And fowls? Had he settled on a site for their house? Was he working on the road to buy furniture for their new home? She could help there, adding shilling to shilling and pound to pound. Oh, how she was looking forward to seeing Christian again, and showing him the start of their fortune. They would build their future together, that they had promised each other. She felt she had made a good start.

What was Christian doing now? When they parted almost

three weeks ago, he had said, 'I'll come and see you at Christmas.' He could say that with confidence, for Friberg had already told the men about their work schedule, and that they would have eight days off over Christmas. Still, how far away was Norsewood? Would he spend his eight days simply walking? Would they have any time together?

In a way, Johanna had been on tenterhooks since she had parted from Christian, her parents and most of her siblings. Her days were full of excitement, but at night, in her small bedroom, her thoughts returned to her family. How were they all? She was sheltered and taken care of, but how were they coping in their open, unprotected world? The only one she knew of was Bertea, her sister two years younger than herself. She, too, had been fortunate in finding work as a domestic servant in Napier. And, thank goodness, she had also gone to a good family. Mr and Mrs Fannin were kind people and they did not demand much of Bertea. After all, she was only slightly older than their only child, Robert. Bertea was like a sister to him, and that's how they wanted to see it. The daughter they had always wanted. Johanna had seen her sister twice already. As luck would have it, they lived quite close and could compare notes.

The first two days in Napier now seemed a haze to Johanna. So much had happened, and with such bewildering speed. Impressions had piled on top of each other, and it took a long time to unscramble them – if they would ever be unscrambled. She remembered coming ashore hand in hand with Christian. Other immigrants followed, and then all milled about.

While the ground was still moving beneath their unsteady feet, they had been confronted by a group of Maori. Brown-skinned people with blue decorations in spirals and curves on their faces. Their feet were bare, although they wore European clothing on the whole, although not – presumably – their Sunday best. They carried sticks. No, not sticks, they were staves, long staves, the type beggars used in Odalen.

The type Old Paso used when he walked from farm to farm.

The small group of men suddenly broke into a dance. They jumped from one foot to the other, always one knee bent, amazingly agile for big, heavy men – so light on their feet. They seemed to be marching fast, but remained on the same spot. The staves were passed from one hand to the other, and back again. Always on the move.

Johanna thought it was a dance. There had been a song too. No, not a song. It was all in the same note like the pastor chanting at Grue Church every Easter Sunday. At one stage, there had been a speech. Perhaps the speech came first. Johanna had lost the sequence of the proceedings. An older man had stepped forward, smaller than the rest, but with more blue spirals on his face. His voice was amazingly strong. There was rhythm in his speech. A set beat. A dance with words.

Years later, Johanna recognised and understood some of the words:

> *Haere mai* . . .
> *Piki mai* . . .
> *Kake mai* . . .
> *E nga manuhiri tuarangi* . . .
> *Ka koa te ngakau* . . .
> *Kua tae mai i tawahi o te ao* . . .

It had been a speech of welcome to the new settlers!

Welcome or not, the immigrants were terrified. Many fled back up the gangway and onto the ship. Children howled. These people were cannibals, the captain had said. Had they come to get the immigrants? Johanna had just stood there, transfixed. Fascinated and frightened at the same time, she clutched Christian's hand to gain strength from him.

Something baffling had happened next. Two guards had appeared, one with a rifle over his shoulder, and the group of Maori was moved on, away from the ship and the port. The tattooed men had felt indignation as well as confusion – to say the least. They had met the 'Yah-yah' people from the *Høvding* the previous year. Those people had seemed friendly enough, although they could only smile shyly and say 'Yah-yah'. So, what was the matter with this lot? Why were they hysterical?

Johanna too, felt confused. Why did the guard have a gun? Had the natives done something dreadful, since they were pushed out of sight? Again, years would pass before she learnt of the civil war in Hawke's Bay. Some were called 'Kupapa', and they had helped the Government. Others were called 'Hau Hau', and they were against the Government. They kept changing sides, so she was told, and no one knew who was who. Was that a reason to treat them roughly?

It took the immigrants quite some time to regain their composure. Then they started taking their possessions up to the disused military barracks at the top of Napier hill, where they slept for the next two nights.

It was late evening on their second day when they were called together to discuss Elliot Greiner's letter. Johanna remembered the tense atmosphere. How could that be forgotten . . . And some details emerged from the haze. Friberg had read out the long letter setting out all Captain Nordby's faults and failings – first in Norwegian, then in English. The letter seemed even longer in that strange sounding language, with all the 'Ss' and hissing sounds. Had they all understood it? Were they all in favour? And were all prepared to sign it? Friberg seemed very keen to bring the Captain to court. And very keen to uphold the dignity and right of the poor passengers who had suffered so much in the hands of this ruthless man.

Johanna had been in two minds about this. Captain Nordby had brought them safely to port. The man understood the wind and the sails, and the strange maps. The men were leaving for Norsewood the next day and would have other thoughts in their heads. So sad about the babies, of course. Still, had there been more deaths aboard this ship than on other immigrant ships?

Johanna learnt a few days later that an inspection had indeed taken place aboard *Høvding*. However, the authorities found nothing wrong with the provisions they saw. The passengers had all looked healthy enough as they came ashore, and had all passed their health inspection on 1 December. Mogstad, the ship's doctor, pointed out that all the deaths had occurred during the first half of the voyage. Clearly, the babies were undernourished before they boarded the ship. What grounds were there for a prosecution?

The men left the next morning, and Johanna retained some vivid memories from that hectic hour. She could still see her mother's eyes filled with anxiety, when she understood she would be left behind with the small children. The other women were in the same situation, and fear was in all faces. How could they defend themselves if cannibals came?

Johanna had seen uncertainty in the men's eyes as they left as well. There were no loud voices this time. No jokes and bravado, as there had been when they set out from Pasotorpet to Christiania. That time they knew the way and felt at ease in their environment. This was something else, they did not know where Norsewood was, nor what would they meet in the deep forests they had heard so much about – and had secretly feared.

She had walked with Christian, hand in hand, behind the barracks – out of sight – before the long caravan set off. There they had held each other, tightly, mouth seeking mouth, bodies pressed against each other. There they stood for a long bittersweet time, until they heard shouts of command and understood the first horse-and-cart loads were on their way.

'I'll come and visit you at Christmas. I should know the way through the forest then. I'll come on *Lille Julaften** if at all possible. I know where you are likely to live.' They

---

* Two days before Christmas Day.

returned, still holding hands, to the front of the barracks. There they saw the caravan was already moving and found the Paso people silently taking their farewells. Johan was holding Randi's hand and looked as if he would not let it go. His son-in-law, Ole, was embracing Berte Maria and their two children. Auntie Karen, Johan's younger sister, was clinging to her Ole, while their four children looked on anxiously.

The women stared after their men long after the party had descended the hill and disappeared behind the bushes, brushwood, scrub and tall grasses. The thick forest that awaited the men was nowhere to be seen.

It was 23 December, and Johanna felt strangely on edge. She and the two girls sat at the dining table. Sheets of paper, pencils and crayons were spread in front of them as usual. It was the thought of Christmas, she had decided, that was upsetting her. How could it be Christmas without snow? Without a tree to decorate? Without carols to practise and small oatmeal cakes to bake? How can it be Christmas in summertime?

Would Christian come? Was it dangerous to walk through the forest? How many days would it take to reach Napier? Would he find the house? She wore her beautiful dress, but had forgotten to put on her apron today.

The Christmas tree posed a problem. She had tried to explain Christmas trees to Jessica and Christina, but they didn't seem to be a tradition in Ny Seland, or at least not in Napier. Words would not do. She did not know enough of them either. The crayons came in handy. One – two – three – a few straight lines, a few curved ones and there was the Christmas tree, with its star on top touching the ceiling. A few wiggly lines and the tree was decorated with streamers. Cut out paper angels followed, with words of explanation and gestures. And there, lo and behold, was the tree almost inside the dining room, and a proper Christmas atmosphere appeared. It should remain inside all through the Christmas period, for 12 whole days, she tried to explain. The trees outside would also be covered in snow.

'Snow?' The two little girls were lost once more.

'Oh, whiter than the clouds spilling over the ranges and floating in the blue sky. Softer and bigger and deeper than the clouds too.'

Johanna's thoughts had crossed the seas and returned to Pasotorpet, where the fir trees were deep in snow. Pangs of homesickness suddenly struck her. How could there be a Christmas without her family, without her parents and her siblings? Without Christian? And these people, nice as they were, didn't have a Christmas tree inside. They didn't even celebrate Christmas Eve, as far as she understood from little Jessica. No holding hands around the Christmas tree, no singing of carols as they walked, turning at every new verse, gazing at the star on top, and thinking about that night in Bethlehem . . . No, nothing like that. Only something the next morning, it seemed. Something noisy without shape and form . . .

She had to pull herself together, or the girls would notice the hot tears that rolled down her cheeks. Perhaps Jessica had noticed something. She pulled Johanna's sleeve.

'Look there, outside the window. We have a Christmas tree in the garden. Just like the one you drew on paper. Can we decorate it?' She was so excited, as she pointed out the window towards the far end of the lawn. There, close to the fence, was a little rimu tree, slender and fragile-looking, with drooping arms.

Johanna was very grateful for this diversion. And when she half closed her eyes, the little rimu did resemble a young fir tree. A little bit at least.

'Quick, we need paper for angels and streamers. Scissors, of course . . . What else? How should we make the star, Christina?' The little girl was too busy sucking her fingers to answer, but Jessica was already out through the door.

❈

Christian had not been alone as he walked through the forest. Fredrik, too, wanted to visit Napier. He wanted to see how his two sisters, Bertea and Johanna, were doing. Although they walked fast, the journey had taken over two days. They had slept at Waipawa and at Paki Paki, and had the good fortune this morning to be offered a ride to Napier with a carrier. A visit to the barber at midday improved their appearances and also lifted their self-confidence. It had cost a whole sixpence to have their hair and beards washed and cut, so they expected to look elegant. Still, that only applied to their heads, the rest was a different story. Their light felt pants from Odalen were now dusty and dirty, and their heavy shirts were far too hot in the Napier summer sunshine. They were very conscious of the smell of sweat, but these were the only clothes they had brought with them, to buy anything new was out of the question.

Even so, money simply flowed from their pockets. It was Yule, and presents were essential. They had combined to buy a bracelet for Bertea. Very nice it was too. Fredrik bought a brooch for Johanna. It looked like the purest gold, but was not as expensive as the look suggested. Christian dug to the very bottom of his pocket. His mission was of the greatest importance, for this Christmas he and Johanna were to become formally engaged. Only the best of gold rings would do, or at least the best his money could buy. And they were expensive – almost two days' wages.

The jeweller was very understanding, although he didn't understand at first that a ring was necessary engagement equipment for Christian to wear as well. The jeweller placed the two rings into a tiny red box, padded with cotton wool, with the utmost care. Money could not be better spent, Christian thought. In his mind's eye, he saw the next scene very clearly. With trembling hands, he would put the ring on Johanna's finger, and she would put the other ring on his finger. And then, then, they would be each other's forever.

'Look, Fredrik, there is a Christmas tree. A Norwegian

Christmas tree!' They had stopped by a low fence and had spotted an unhappy looking rimu tree festooned with paper garlands. Its poor top was weighed down with . . . hard to say, but it could have been a star made of cardboard.

'Do we dare knock on the door?'

'No, no! Let's wait here. Perhaps Johanna will see us and come out . . .' They did not know how to deal with this. What would the rich people inside think of them if they knocked on their door? Would they think they were beggars, vagabonds perhaps? They were sure to look down on them as they looked so untidy. If the Cornfords opened the door quickly, these rich people may well get a fright. They could call the police or . . . or . . . just shoo them away.

They lent against the garden fence, staring hopefully at the verandah with the open French door. Long white curtains filled much of the space on either side, blowing like sails, but as light as cobwebs. You could see through them perhaps. It was so stately and strange. So distant in a way; almost like being in a church, and one didn't talk in a church. How did Johanna like living here? Had all this finery changed her? That was the door she would be coming through. The one facing them with the fluttering angel wings . . .

And then Johanna came through the open door with the angel wings, quickly and nimbly, on her way to pick flowers for Mrs Cornford to arrange.

'Christian, Fredrik!' She leaped from the verandah. A few further leaps and she was by the fence and holding their hands.

'Oh, at long last! How wonderful to see you Christian, and you too Fredrik.' Three pairs of hands were firmly clasped.

'Come on in.' A few more quick leaps and she had opened the garden gate for the young men. No, she had not changed, thank God. The big white house, the rich people and all the finery . . . No, it had not spoilt her.

The garden was full of flowers and dappled sunshine,

flowers by the verandah, in beds, around the corner, along the next wall of the house. Full of good scent and a feeling of peace. Above all there was peace. The men fell silent once more, not from awkwardness this time, but from a sense of luxury.

Johanna led them to a bench in a shaded part of the garden, still firmly holding Christian's hand. She wanted to hear all the news from Norsewood.

Yes, greetings and love, and Christmas wishes from all members of the Paso family. The women and children had arrived there safely a few days ago after an arduous journey. They still lived in communal accommodation. No, very little space, water was quite a problem, and sanitation was not the best. It took more than a few weeks to build a house, although a good start had been made by most. Yes, there was a shop, and credit would be given. Friberg had seen to that.

The Greiner family? No. They seemed unlikely to last long. Elliot had taken one look at the Norsewood jungle and the huge trees, and had said he could do better than that. He must have had some money in his pocket, because the family had begun planning to leave almost immediately.

Christian had stopped at that point. There was no purpose in telling Johanna that Elliot intended to make his way to Australia, and was urging people to go there with him.* Some may have been sorely tempted, however, with no money it was out of the question. Elliot had been very angry with Friberg, not just over the land, but for not taking Captain Nordby to court.

Johanna seemed to have been reading his thoughts. 'How do people get on with Friberg?'

Christian hesitated. It was difficult to give a clear answer, as the picture was so confused. Some liked Friberg and trusted him – including Johan and Ole. Many others felt

---

* The Greiner family subsequently settled in Gisborne. They moved to Australia in about 1883.

the opposite, but those sentiments were mixed, and were blended with envy and – perhaps – jealousy.

'I think it will sort itself out in the end.' He had pondered the question for some time. 'True, the feeling is that he misled us, promised something that did not exist. One thing is sure, there is no point in keeping attitudes of blame and animosity alive. We have been placed here and might as well make the best of it.' Johanna looked at him with admiration. How good and wise he was. How well he spoke!

Christian became very animated when it came to their house site. It was just about ready – nice and even too. He would fell the trees for timber early in the new year, using the best of rimu and totara, and would build a house big enough for twelve children. And would she believe it, there was already a building on the site. The type they called a *whare*. Not for her to sleep in though! Oh, no! It was only four metres square and made of ponga logs placed upright, side by side. The type of logs that would not burn, a spiky one they call *wheki*. A floor too, that was a double layer of the same material. Good to sleep on and quite springy.

Did he sleep there?

Well . . . Just sometimes, when not doing road work the next morning. So he could get an early start on bush work. It was meant as a shed for all his tools – axes, saws and slashers. It would make a good fowl house one day. And he cooked outside on a fire with a camp oven.* Christian, normally a man of few words, felt quite hot.

'How is Papa?' Johanna felt uneasy. Johan had not been mentioned. Christian hesitated and Fredrik came to the rescue. Between them, they managed to convey the message that Johan had been quite overcome when he saw the huge trees on his block of land. Clearing it all and establishing his farming kingdom had suddenly become a daunting, near impossible task.

---

* A heavy cast iron pot with a lid.

After some days of pondering, and virtual silence, Johan had declared he would dispose of most of his land, and establish himself as a blacksmith and wheelwright. There had been support from unexpected quarters. Friberg, when consulted, had been very enthusiastic. The village needed a blacksmith – badly – and the local carts, drays and wagons could be improved upon. The wheels were clumsily made and not really suitable for the conditions. Friberg was prepared to advance finance to get Johan started. This would be for a house, workshop and equipment. The next supporter was Johan's own son-in-law, Ole Olsen, Berte Maria's husband. He also viewed the farming prospects darkly and wanted to be Johan's partner in the new business venture.

Perhaps most importantly of all was the encouragement from Randi and Berte Maria. They were shocked when they first encountered the Seventy-Mile-jungle. Still, they fully understood, like the other immigrant wives, that there was no retreat or return. They must accept what was there and make the best of it. And it was in their blood anyway, to give their husbands every ounce of support. Accept and adapt, Randi kept saying to herself. Accept and adapt – as she brushed many silent tears from her eyes. A forge that could earn money straightaway for food and clothing was a good idea.

Johan was optimistic once more, but his voice was more subdued than in the past. Twenty acres would do him nicely, as well as Ole. They could clear and stock the land at their leisure. There would no longer be any urgency. The main thing was to get the smithy going, so cash would start flowing. The future now looked quite rosy, thanks to Friberg.

There was one more item of news from Norsewood, and Christian had purposely kept it to the last.

'Your Mama and Papa have a very special Christmas gift for you.' Johanna looked up, all anticipation.

'The spinning wheel, Randi's spinning wheel. But you

cannot have it, they say, before you move into our new home at Norsewood.'

The two little girls, Jessica and Christina, had ventured ever so slowly down the verandah. Then they had edged their way across the lawn, towards the two visitors with their strange language and peculiar smell. Christina's fingers did not leave her mouth.

'How do you do, girls?' Fredrik was trying out his linguistic skills.

'Very well, thank you. How do you do?' Jessica wanted to initiate a conversation, but Fredrik's social vocabulary was exhausted.

Johanna was very well aware her young men were in need of a good wash.

'Take your boots off boys. I'll get you some soap and water – and your shirts too. The girls won't mind.' Moments later she was back with a bucket of rainwater from the tank stand.

Oh, the luxury of a good wash! First their necks and upper parts of their bodies, then their poor feet that had covered so many long kilometres in the last few days. If only they had something else to wear instead of their smelly shirts. But who could consider that after less than three weeks of work – and engagement rings! Johanna, wonderful Johanna, who understood everything had anticipated their thoughts, and had already dashed inside. There, from the top drawer of her dresser, she fished out something of great value.

The two hand-sewn shirts had been made over the last fortnight. Both had been meant for Christian, as she thought he would be on his own. A quick decision – the plain shirt for Fredrik, the one with the embroidered bear in the Skara forest for Christian. Highly suitable, she thought. What luck that Johanna had managed two shirts.

'Here. An early Christmas present for you two. Slip them on and see if they fit.' How could anything be so shiny and white, so cool and fresh looking – and fit so well? More than words were needed here. Johanna was kissed, in front of the little girls who tactfully backed away, for a moment only.

The timing was good. Mrs Cornford appeared in the garden moments later, striding across the lawn with out-stretched hands. No, not the least bit haughty or conde-scending. No, absolutely not looking down on them. Tactful too, bless her. She had obviously seen the two dusty shirts across the back of the garden bench, as a rapid conversation with Johanna followed. How that lady could talk! And smile and nod and laugh at the same time. It was all meaningless to the two young men in their lovely white shirts. They now suffered a brief spell of shyness. Johanna tried to interpret, but had her difficulties. Something was clear – that Betty would love to see her relatives from Norsewood. Betty must come for dinner. Would Johanna go to Fannins' and ask nicely? 'Betty' meant Bertea – and was a brave attempt to master a new name.

Christian and Fredrik were ushered inside. They were to have a cup of tea. A nice cup of tea – after their long dusty journey. There was nothing like a cup of tea to revive a person. So refreshing. Men in particular felt that. Do sit down.

The children had followed their mother into the kitchen. The door was closed behind them. Talking could be heard, laughter and giggles, clattering of china and an oven door opened and closed. What was taking place there? The two young men felt uneasy in their deep leather chairs. It was all too much. Striped wallpaper, up and down the wall, pictures on the walls too, carpets on the floor, and cabinets along the wall with glass doors. And inside the cabinets, multi-coloured cups and saucers and small plates. All were so fragile looking one did not dare to move. No, they were not feeling comfortable in their comfortable chairs. Legs were crossed and uncrossed, in spite of the fragile china that kept staring at them from behind the glass doors. Where is Johanna? Why is she so long?

It was Mrs Cornford, with her cups of tea, who came to the rescue. Handling cups and saucers was a challenge, and to cope with biscuits at the same time was a doubtful pleasure. Still, somehow Mrs Cornford made them feel at ease. Was it her presence, her smiles perhaps, or was it her tea? The fidgeting stopped. The men relaxed, and the fancy cups in the china cabinet ceased their haughty stare. Mrs Cornford had a soothing influence, a calming manner. She spoke slowly and clearly, leaning slightly forward in her chair, and looked them straight in the face. The smile was always there, on her lips or at the back of her eyes. She seemed so interested in them and wanted to hear about the big trees.

Shyness evaporated as dew before the dawn. Christian thought he understood most of what was said; her gestures were easy to follow and very helpful as well. He launched into a speech about the virtues of rimu and totara, their height, their ages, their girth, and which was used for what. To explain this he pointed in turn to the floor, the walls and the windows. Perhaps his hands were more eloquent that his tongue, but she nodded and smiled and seemed to have no difficulties in understanding.

Encouraged by her warm smiles and eyes, Christian wanted to embark on a more ambitious topic; to tell her about his and Johanna's future home. That could well have overtaxed his verbal and manual skills, but at this point Johanna and 'Betty' burst into the room. Jack Cornford, home from his legal office, followed them and the atmosphere changed.

Demonstrative sibling affection had never been part of Pasotorpet make-up. Bertea must have undergone a change – or had she forgotten all the family decorum and restraint? She shamelessly threw her arms around Fredrik in front of everyone, and her big brother failed to defend himself. He was even seen to hold onto her for a split second. Johanna and Christian looked at each other with eyes that asked – when will our turn come? No, not here. Later.

'Sherry, Jane! Sherry for our guests.' Jack Cornford had a booming voice. A bit like Captain Nordby, Christian thought for a horrible moment. He didn't order the sherry. As a man of action, he went to the fragile looking glass cabinet himself. From it, he removed some even more fragile looking glasses that gave a high-pitched pinging sound when they touched each other.

Christian and Fredrik had never tasted sherry before and soon felt relaxed. At the point when they were teaching Jack to say *Skål*, he was called into the kitchen for consultation. He reappeared carrying two pairs of pants, light-coloured and summery looking, and of generous dimensions around the waist.

'The girls would like to wash your clothes, I hear. Perhaps you could wear these in the meantime? You can change in the summerhouse if you like. That's out in the garden. I believe your beds have been made up there.' There was no end to the family's kindness, tact and understanding.

A relaxed group of people enjoyed dinner that summer evening. Host and hostess with their two small children, two young domestic servants and two young men from the bush in their clean clothes. The tiny box with the red lining and gold rings had been transferred to another pocket. Christian kept checking it was safe. This was 23 December, *Lille Julaften*, the day before Christmas Eve, in the year of our Lord 1873.

Eileen Williams, of Kelburn, Wellington, heard many stories about her grandmother as a child. She loved to visit her in Norsewood, to sit on her lap and to listen to the many tales about the early settlers. The story that moved her most, though, was that of her ancestors' first Christmas in New Zealand. A midsummer Christmas without snow!

'I have never experienced a white Christmas, and in a strange way, I feel I have missed something important. Perhaps it is because of Grandma's stories – or do you think it's in our blood? We who came from the land of reindeer, snow and trolls?'

The delightful old lady looked at me questioningly. There were pieces in her life's jigsaw puzzle that were missing, and she did not seem to know what they were. She was almost 80 years old now and considered it too late to examine her ancestral roots.

'I know that Grandma missed having Christmas with snow. The Ruahine Ranges also have snow, but at the wrong time of the year. She brought her traditions with her from home, but none seemed stronger than those linked with Christmas. They celebrated Christmas Eve in Norsewood in those days. That tradition died out. So sad . . .'

'And she had special Christmas dishes. We descendants have forgotten most details, and we are poorer for that. However, we know she never cooked or ate pork because of the reference in the Bible to pigs being dirty.' Favourite dishes she made have been passed down, though, and Eileen still makes waffles (*Vafler*), beef meatballs (*Kjottboller*) and a shortbread type of biscuit with a jam filling.

Eileen also knew that her grandparents became engaged the first Christmas in New Zealand.

'That was before the real hardship started. I think it was a happy time for them both.'

It was Boxing Day 1873, and Christian and Fredrik were heading back to Norsewood. The trunk of a totara tree, its bark hanging in coarse, cascading sheets, made a convenient backrest for the tired travellers. Both were now half-asleep in the midday sun. They again wore the clothes they had worn on the outward journey. The shirts and trousers from Napier were far too good for dust, grime and sweat stains. What a generous family the Cornfords had been! Jack had refused to take his trousers back.

'No, no, they fit you, and they suit you too. You would do me a favour to keep them. Please!' In no way did he indicate how desperately sorry he felt for the young men returning to Norsewood. Unlike his wife, who had romantic notions about life in the bush, Jack foresaw a future of toil, hardship and poverty.

Christian was filled with deep gratitude. Above all, he had gained a glimpse into another world. A world where people lived well, were kind, generous and understanding, and could be all these things without being patronising. He would remember this Christmas all his life. It had been packed with invaluable experiences. What luck. What indescribable luck, that Johanna had come to this family where she could absorb so much, she who had such capacity for learning.

Johanna. Oh, how he would miss her! His heart pounded at the thought of her. He wanted to relive all the agonising and beautiful moments they had spent together these last few days. She had been so delighted with the spinning wheel. So thrilled, so eager to start using it. Where should it be placed in their new house? The engagement ring! Moments of utter happiness and bliss! How surprised she had been. Still, could she not have expected something like that? He looked at his own gold ring that Johanna had placed on his right hand. Happiness for life.

The farewell had been difficult. He had felt her firm breasts pressing against him. His left hand had strayed – from her head and neck, and down her body.

'No Christian. Not here. Not now. In our own home. Be good to me. Please!' They had kissed again. Locked in one long, everlasting kiss.

'When do you think the house will be finished?' She had whispered so sweetly. Christian had hesitated. It was not just the house, but the bush as well. This dense, agonising forest with the huge trees.

'The house I'll start on straightaway. But the jungle is so huge. It will take many years to clear.'

'Many years?' She was not whispering now. It was more like a shout, a cry of disbelief and despair. Many years? Is it really as bad as that? Yes, it was as bad as that. So bad that he was close to losing heart, but he did not tell her that. With Johanna at his side, he would conquer the 40 acres – and much, much more.

'Hmm. I was thinking of the whole block. That will take some time. A paddock, a cow, some hens, a garden though . . . Well, I could do that tomorrow.' He tried to sound light-hearted, but did not quite succeed. She squeezed his hand.

'Don't wear yourself out, dear Christian. Not for my sake. Time is on our side. We need to save a bit. Do you know how much I have in my drawer?' She had looked up, quite excited and proud of herself. 'I have 18 shillings! The longer I stay with the Cornfords, the more we will save. I can wait for you Christian. You will always be my whole world . . .'

Wonderful Johanna. Warm waves of tenderness had passed through him, one after the other. He felt dizzy. Her longings were as strong as his. Still, she was so sensible, so clear-sighted. She would wait for him even if it took months, years perhaps.

'I must not forget, Johanna, that if we struggle, we are doing this for our children. The whole dozen of them. It will be our own land, our own farm in the end. Something we could never have managed at Grue, or in Odalen.' She had kissed him once again, full of understanding.

7 'Our daily bread'

S IGGA and Johan have lived in New Zealand for just over fifty years, the last three decades in the leafy, garden-conscious part of Palmerston North known as Hokowhitu. She has Icelandic roots (and name) and is from Tønsberg, where SS *Høvding* was built. He is a retired schoolteacher, from Ljan, Oslo, who 'explored' New Zealand as early as 1947.

They became my special helpers and consultants with Project Johanna Johansdatter. I don't know how many days and nights I spent in their home. All material gathered was sifted, sorted, discussed, discarded or arranged, in their garden, or at their dining table.

I was constantly reminded not to overlook the role of women in Norsewood. Without their courage and doggedness, life there would have been very miserable. They were the real heart of their families. Milking the cows, looking after the stock, looking after the house and garden, bringing up the children, and often putting courage back into their dispirited and unemployed men.

Pictures in the Norsewood Pioneer Museum tell very much the same tale.

❁

It was early December 1880. Soon it would be mid-summer in the Seventy-Mile-Bush. The days were longer, more sun and light reached the ground. The sky was visible where small cottages stood amidst fallen logs. Here the landscape resembled a battlefield. Giants slain but not buried, while sheep and cattle grazed among their black corpses. Where the huge rimu, totara, miro and matai reigned, though, very little light reached the forest floor. The sky remained out of sight. Bush clearing had not been done systematically or consistently. It was done in fits and starts, when husbands and sons could spare the time from paid work or other chores.

Work on the roads and, until recently, on the railway being built through the district, sapped the men's strength. Often they worked far from home, wife and children. They living in cramped and damp conditions, usually under canvas with limited variety of food – not that this latter problem was too different from when they were at home. Johanna had accepted this. From the very first day she understood. This work pattern was not to be broken. Even though Christian did not like to be away from home for long, it could be a whole week, or even two, before he reappeared. And then he was away again after a couple of hectic days and nights. Not much could be achieved on their own block of land in that way.

Johanna drew a deep sigh. She could allow herself that, when she was alone. With her husband at home she could not, must not, show any sign of disenchantment. He needed encouragement. The change from the Cornford's spacious villa in Napier, to the slab cottage facing the road between Napier and Manawatu,* had not been easy. She did not show her disappointment when she first saw that grey hut. Its roughly sawn totara planks were placed vertically, while the

---

* This is now State Highway Two. The property adjoined present-day Gundries Road, and was opposite Garfield Road, which in turn was then called Friberg Road.

cracks between the boards were covered with battens. So humble and forlorn, it looked as if it was apologising for its own existence. And to think that those noble trees, which had stood only metres away, had been converted into this thing. Her old home at Pasotorpet had been much better than this! She did not weep, as she knew other wives had done, at the sight of what should have been their wonderful home in this new land. No, why should she? This was only the beginning. In a year or two, when they were better off and looked out on fenced paddocks and gardens, everything would be much better. Then they would build a proper house – and employ a proper builder as well. They had both agreed on that.

It was almost five years since they had moved into their humble home. Had anything changed for the better? The cottage still had only two rooms, one for general use – a sitting room, they liked to call it – and one bedroom. Then, of course, there was the ponga whare Christian had built in 1873. Still with its canvas roof, and almost unchanged except that it now housed six hens and a rooster, as well as Christian's heavy tools.

Their own roof was as grey as their cottage. It was covered with shingles, split from straight totara blocks, around 40 cm long. Oh! Such a painstaking job to produce these thin slats of wood, and even more to replace the damaged ones on the roof. Dear Christian, he had worked so hard – and had really achieved so much during those two years she had been with the Cornfords in Napier. The fireplace, on one of the end walls of the single-gabled cottage, was lined with papa clay. The chimney was a combination of stones, clay, ponga logs and two sheets of iron – so expensive – but it drew beautifully. It was a pleasure to cook in the fireplace, especially when using the heavy camp ovens. Well . . . almost a pleasure. Christian had been so clever building the fire-place. It had just the right depth and height.

The cottage was not without furniture. There was a

kitchen bench and a cupboard. Adolf's tool kit from Steinbekken had come in very handy. Best of all was the long table made from one thick slab of rimu, and almost as big and beautiful as the table at Pasotorpet. Instead, though, it was a reddish colour, not bleached white with wood ash and endless rubbings with sandstone, like the table at 'home'. Christian had put all his love and skill into making this table – and into his plans for the future. It was obvious he hoped for many children and the table was to be the family centre. Here they would talk, learn, play board games, study, discuss . . . and do more than just eat together.

There was one long form, also Christian's work, placed by the wall. However, the four chairs had been bought – bought with Johanna's savings from Napier. She was so proud of these chairs. Even more proud than she had been of her cutlery and china. Everything inside the cupboard had come with her from Napier, had been her achievement in a sense. Not that she had bought it all. No, far from it. The Cornford family had been so generous, so unbelievably kind to them. The little cupboard could not hold all her treasures from Napier. Much was stored in boxes under their bed – and much had already been given away – as engagement presents, at weddings or at christenings. Especially at christenings, which occurred often in Norsewood.

Oh, the bed. The huge sturdy bed that hid so many treasures and secrets, was also one of Christian's master-pieces. It was the only piece of furniture in the bedroom, shelves, wardrobe and dresser were still to come. Still to come! That had been the situation all these years.

A deep sigh, once more. When would the good times come? When would they be able to live in a proper house? Their courage had not weakened, nor their determination, but it seemed impossible to make plans. There was never enough time or money.

Times had changed – a change for the worse. For the first few years, there had been work opportunities for most able-bodied men in Norsewood. A whole network of roads had spread throughout the Seventy-Mile-Bush. The railway creeping slowly from Napier towards the Manawatu Gorge had reached Kopua in 1878. There it encountered the first of the deep gullies and unstable terrain that had struck fear into the hearts of engineers. Those charged with paying for the huge viaducts, and repairing the damage caused when slips repeatedly destroyed in moments the work of months, watched as the money – and the lives of a few labourers – slipped away.

Then, in early August 1880, just as the railway stations opened at Ormondville and the new railhead at Makotuku (at the far end of Friberg [now Garfield] Road) the Government announced the next section of railway would not continue just yet. The Norsewood people were bitterly disappointed. They had waited years for the station to open at Ormondville, as it would save them the longer trip to Kopua. Many, however, had also counted on a few more years of work on the line between Makotuku and Tahoraiti, beyond Dannevirke. Angry protest meetings occurred around the district. But it was very hard to impress upon the authorities just how hard things were for the people struggling to live in the Seventy-Mile-Bush.

The daily pay was always five shillings. Now suddenly, virtually overnight, things had changed. The Government's coffers were empty, and it was necessary to save. Most public works ceased and many men found themselves unemployed. Existence had been hand to mouth before, and people were always on a tight budget. But now, during this depression, stark poverty stared them in the face. The fortunate ones who found work had to be satisfied with four shillings per day. A callous take-it-or-leave-it attitude prevailed. Money had to be found, or else . . . and there were more and more mouths to feed at home.

The Norsewood men scattered in search of work. Some

went to Napier and took what work was offered. Others went to Palmerston North and beyond. Some tried their hands at seasonal work on farms and sheep stations. They all had one thing in common – there was little cash to show for their long, hard weeks away.

Family life suffered during the depression and the heart of the family suffered the most. It was left to the mothers to feed, clothe and raise the children, to extend the vegetable garden. To do further bush felling, so another cow or a few more sheep could be added to the stock numbers, or create another patch of earth where grass could be grown and then harvested for its highly saleable seed. Their working day was long and hard. They encouraged each other, not just with words, but also with little household gifts that came from the heart – and went to the heart. Eggs, milk, peaches, vegetables . . . even seed potatoes were passed across the fence, usually by children, who also had a message to deliver. 'Mother says we cannot use them. You would do her a favour to take them off her hands.'

When it came to hand-me-down clothes, only mothers could handle this. 'My Ellen has outgrown this old, home-spun jersey. Do you think it could fit your Justine?'

The bonds of support were strong between the mothers, but it may well have been Johanna's English lessons that forged the strongest links. The mothers met once a week to learn English. Johanna understood very well that without this language, life in the bush would be even more difficult and lonely. It was amazing what she had absorbed in Napier over two years, and she had also obtained an English Grammar. I am like Old Paso, my grandfather, she thought. This passion for sharing, for passing on the little I know, must come from him.

Seven years had passed since they arrived in New Zealand. How quickly that time had slipped away. It had not been all hardship and struggle. Oh no! There had been pleasures and excitement for the former Paso family too. Surely their wedding in February 1876 had been the high point. Then came the birth of their little girl nine months later, with Randi and Berte Maria – mother and sister – as midwives. Oh, that was something else to remember with extreme pleasure. At least it was after the labour pains ceased.

Johanna's happiness had not lasted long. Only two months later, she had lost her father to consumption. The last Johan of Pasotorpet was only 46 years old. He was not the first to go. That insidious illness seemed to have accompanied them to Norsewood as well. It had claimed both young and old – and the small ones, undernourished and weak, seemed to have been an easy target for death. Women seemed to fare better than men. Are we really stronger? Johanna wondered. Are we able to resist infection better? Or is it because the men's work meant they got cold and wet more often?

And yes, there had been scars from the bad times aboard *Høvding* and scars from the bad times before *Høvding*! Doubtless too, there were more scars from those first months in Norsewood when food was scarce and – in particular – when the available food was unattractive to very young children. Certainly, much of it was not very nutritious. For adults and older children this phase perhaps passed without long-term effect. However, for a young child whose small body was at a vital stage of development during that time, things could be very different. And so, when the time came for precious little Julius to carry his own body-weight, this weight was far too heavy for his softened leg bones. They bent very badly and remained that way for the rest of his life. He had developed rickets.

There were a number of widows in Norsewood. And most were badly off, no matter how much compassion, help and support they received from neighbours. However, a sensible arrangement eased their plight and many a young bachelor soon found himself in holy matrimony – complete with an instant family. And, of course, employment on the Public Works schemes that did exist around this time could only be offered to married men. These marriages may not have been based entirely on love, but they had their purpose.

Randi grieved deeply. She and Johan had knitted themselves into a close team, but life had to go on. And little Julius needed a father. So, before the year was up, she was married again. Hans Andersen, a Dane, was the shopkeeper at Makaretu, some kilometres north of Norsewood. His wife had died and his grown children had flown the nest – and Randi was known as a capable worker. Julius might be useful too when he was a little older. The wedding was a quiet affair without festivities of any sort. That was what Hans, as well as Randi, had wanted. Twelve months later, Randi was a widow once more. Consumption had claimed her second husband as well.

'No more! Never again,' said an embittered Randi Finnsdatter. 'From now on I shall look after myself! Julius and myself!' The two younger girls, Randine and Karen, were still with her, but they were sure to follow in the footsteps of their older sisters into domestic service. So with the money left to her, Randi bought a small property on the main road, just north of Norsewood.* There was enough money for a cow, some sheep and a pig as well. She was a good midwife and found plenty of use for her skills. This, and knitting, also gave her a small income. When necessary, she called on Berte Maria and Johanna to assist.

Johanna felt Randi's loss keenly. What could she do for her mother? Or for poor Julius? Each week, when Johanna conducted her English class, Randi and Julius walked along the Napier road to stay at Johanna's place on the opposite side of Norsewood. Johanna tried to return the visits from time to time, but her hands were full. It was never easy to get away from home.

* The cottage is still there.

Pasotorpet soon after relocation to its present site, and its subsequent conversion to a stable, in the late 1920s. At that time, iron was installed over the shingle roof.
(Photo: Johanna Christiansen, this copy, Val Burr, Palmerston North)

Overlooking the track down Pasoberget (Paso Hill) from Pasotorpet, with Meitsjøen (Lake Meit) in the distance.
(Photo: Øystein Molstad Andresen, Hamar, Norway)

The farmhouse and outbuildings at Kuggerud Farm, in Nord-Odal, from an old postcard. The Pasotorpet family gathered here en route to Christiania (Oslo) to board *Høvding*.
(Photo: Mimi and Arne Løfsgaard, Kuggerud Farm, Norway)

Høvding configured as a sailing ship, as it was during its voyages to New Zealand. Another painting after its conversion to a barque in 1882 helped fuel the mistaken belief there were two *Høvdings*.
(Photo: Dannevirke Scandinavian Club)

Norsewood under snow, between 1882 when the Lutheran Church was completed and 1888 when it burnt down. The Junction Hotel is at the extreme left. The school, in Upper Norsewood, is in the distance. This is the scene through which the 1888 fire raged.
(Photo: Norsewood Pioneer Museum)

The Salvation Army Barracks in Lower Norsewood. The full-bearded man near the right appears to be Christian.
(Photo: Norsewood Pioneer Museum)

The official opening of Norsewood's second dairy factory, the
Norsewood Dairy Co. Ltd., which commenced operations
in February 1897.
(*Photo: From a copy held by Norsewood Pioneer Museum*)

Lower Norsewood, in the first years of the twentieth century.
Distinctive features are the second Lutheran Church and the Junction
Hotel, surrounded by large trees near the right side.
(*Photo: From a postcard at Norsewood Pioneer Museum*)

After Johan's tragic death in 1899, and with Hannah on the way, Johanna thought it timely to commission a family photograph. From left: (back row) Martin, Fred, Joseph, Carl, Rolf, Rangna. (Middle row) Eva, Christian, Arthur, Johanna, Enoch. (Front Row) Daniel, Sarah.
(Photo: From a copy held by Norsewood Pioneer Museum)

Sawmill workers at a Seventy-Mile-Bush camp in the 1890s. Sitting, (fourth from right) is Christian, wearing his trademark Salvation Army jersey and hat. While not identified individually, it is believed his sons Johan, Joseph, Carl August and Rolf, along with Uncle Julius (arms crossed, centre row, second from left) are also in the group.
(Photo: Norsewood Pioneer Museum.)

Sawmilling in the Norsewood-Ormondville area around the 1890s. The Christiansen men earned their living in just such an environment.
(Photo: Dannevirke Gallery of History)

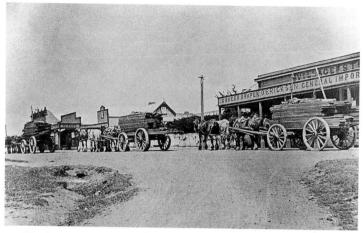

Heavily laden timber wagons outside Ericksen's store in Upper Norsewood. Although the road appears dry and smooth, in winter the heavy wagons caused considerable damage to roads.
(Photo: From a copy held by Dannevirke Gallery of History)

Norsewood's 1922 Golden Jubilee celebrated the arrival of its first immigrants on 20 September 1872. Some of the original pioneers are: from left: (back row) Ole Lund, O. O. Nordbye, C. E. Pettersen, E. A. Laurvig, Emanuel Frederickson, Christian Christiansen, Knud Andersen. (Front row) Ole Johansen, Mrs Mandell, Mrs Ole Gundersen, Mrs Jens Neilsen, Mrs Hans Olsen, Mrs Ole Christiansen, Mrs Peter Larsen, Mrs John Petersen, Mrs Theodor Andreassen, Mrs Herbert and Mrs (Johanna) Christiansen.
(Photo: Nor 3, Tararua Library Trust, Dannevirke)

Johanna and Christian, surrounded by many of their descendents,
during their Diamond Wedding celebrations in 1936.
(Photo: Eileen Williams, Kelburn)

Johanna poses with her 18-year-old granddaughter Eileen Andersen
(Williams), her beloved spinning wheel and examples of her
handiwork during the Diamond Wedding celebrations.
(Photo: Eileen Williams, Kelburn)

Johanna's three children, Rangna aged 4, Carl August aged 3, and little Johan, just over 1, needed a lot of attention. She also had to keep an eye on their growing flock of sheep and her two cows, as they might easily wander into the forest. Daisy and Rosy – named after the Pasotorpet cows – were supposed to graze around the house, but the fences were not the best. The only securely fenced paddock needed some attention as well. Their potatoes and other vegetables grew there, and these needed weeding from time to time. Everything grew so fast here, especially the weeds. Sometimes wild pigs, and how Johanna disliked pigs, attempted to break in. Then the fences would need repairing and strengthening. In the evenings, with the children in bed, she would take the spinning wheel and find a place on the floor where it could stand firmly. It was Pasotorpet all over again! Only this time it was not Johanna, but her children, who fell asleep to the music of the spinning wheel.

How she had blessed that Christmas gift from her parents! It had come in handy from the first day of her marriage. As well as wool from their own sheep, Christian, thoughtful Christian, sometimes brought a bag of brown wool home when he returned from work. Such wool was of little value to the farmers, but Johanna treasured it for knitting patterns. One day, she told herself, when she had time, she would start dying wool again. How would that lovely lichen already growing on the fence posts be? Honey-coloured perhaps? Balls of wool and knitted jerseys and socks followed. Some were given away, some bartered for shoes, fencing materials and a spade – and some even found their way into the Norsewood General Store. What did she have to complain about? Mr and Mrs Christiansen had made a good start in New Zealand, compared with so many others.

A good start or not, they felt the depression, and Christian had to travel further away to find work. At those times it was good to be busy all day. It was when she sat by the spinning wheel and heard it humming his name, or in the big bed missing the warmth of his body . . . It was then she especially longed for her Christian.

She was spinning when she suffered her first coughing attack. It was so violent she had to stand, hunched almost double beside the spinning wheel. Her chest was in agony by the time the attack ended.

She too? Had she also been infected? Visions of horror confronted her and continued to pursue her every night. She saw herself in a coffin. Christian and the children were there too. She saw their huge eyes, faces washed with tears. Dear God, is this the way I shall go? She was frightened. Really frightened. Should the future collapse just like that? Had the breath from her father, with that dreadful odour, passed into her lungs?

Poor Papa! He had been so delighted when she came to Norsewood in 1875 to celebrate Christmas. It was the first time she had been there, but she had come to stay. The wedding was to take place in February. She and Christian had decided on that when he arrived in Napier to collect her. She hardly recognised her father when she saw him. So thin and pale, it was hard to look at him. Christian had warned her he had been poorly lately, and Ole, her brother-in-law, mainly worked by himself in the smithy these days. Still, she had not been prepared for what she saw. She did not let on and he did not mention his illness either. He had been all laughter and gaiety when she had entered her parents' little house south of the village.

'Finally! How we have missed you Johanna . . . You won't be allowed to leave us again.' He had taken hold of her hands, held onto them firmly. 'When the bells toll for your wedding, you'll be a farmer's wife, here in Norsewood. I'll give you away. That's something I have been looking forward to for a long time, I can tell you that.'

It had not been a big wedding. The marquee rigged up for the occasion consisted of ponga tree logs supporting a canvas roof and canvas walls. The marquee was packed with relations, old friends from Odalen and new friends from around the district. There was hardly any aisle left, and Johan and Johanna almost had to push their way through to the homemade altar. Oh, how proud Johan had been. The pastor had blessed it all that morning, the altar as well as the canvas enclosing it, so the rough construction had become a holy church for the occasion.

At the far end of the holy church tent stood a hot and nervous Christian. Fredrik, at his side, stood erect and at attention like a Prussian grenadier. Seated opposite, were Randi and Berte Maria, both beaming with anticipation.

The marriage ceremony was to be conducted by a Methodist minister,* but the good Lutherans were not greatly upset by this. This minister was Norwegian; and what's more, he had almost been a neighbour when they left in 1873. And now, God be praised, he was here. He had followed them across the ocean and was living just outside Norsewood.

Edward Nielsen was 32 years of age in 1874 when he felt the call and had set out as a missionary. He had worked as a Methodist preacher in Hamar and Furnes, before moving to Sør-Odal. In that district, many people had recently cut their ties with the Lutheran State Church to join his Methodist church. And, of course, some of his newfound flock there had emigrated to New Zealand. Johanna had heard of him and knew there had been conflict and theological tussles between the Lutheran pastor and the new preacher back in Norway, but that was all she knew.

There were no such arguments in Norsewood. Reverend Nielsen was one of them. And, quite simply, there were still no Lutheran pastors in New Zealand for him to clash with. So, he had been very warmly welcomed when he rode into the village in 1875. Had he not made the hazardous trip from Palmerston North – across swollen rivers and through

---

* At this time Scandinavian Methodists were referred to as Scandinavian Wesleyans.

the mud-filled quagmire that was referred to as a road? Had he not done this just because he wanted to serve his kinsmen? Theological hairsplitting had not been practiced here. Marriage was marriage, and God was God, no matter who officiated.

Even so, it was reassuring to know Reverend Nielsen was a fully qualified man of God. He had been ordained in Palmerston North, at the newly built Methodist Church, shortly before leaving for Norsewood. People appreciated being ministered to by a Norwegian, especially one who had acquired some of the genuine Odalen dialect. Johanna was overjoyed. Surely this was a sign their marriage was blessed in heaven.

After they had said 'Yes' and 'I will' and had promised each other fidelity in both good and bad days, everyone went outside to the warm February sunshine. The landscape was littered with logs, interspersed with a few cows and some sheep on the next hill. And ever present were the dark and brooding Ruahine Ranges. Saws and axes had yet to bite into their flanks, but did they plot revenge for the violation of their gaunt and ravaged foothills?

Reverend Nielsen had mounted his horse and bade fond farewells to the young couple. It had all been so solemn. No, he could not stay for the formalities that followed. He had pressing business to attend to at Makaretu.

What a transformation! In a few minutes the makeshift marquee had changed from a church to a hall. Gone were two canvas walls and gone was the altar. Instead two long tables had appeared, heavy planks across sawhorses. Oh, God! For a dreadful moment, Fredrik revisited the funerals at sea. But, like magic, the table runners appeared. Then came the tantalising odours from various pots and pans, billies and camp ovens, plates and platters, and assorted dishes big and small. And bottles appeared on the table. Some contained genuine beer purchased from the district's few licensed accommodation houses. Other bottles housed more nondescript contents, the origin of which was some-what less certain! No one came empty-handed to Johanna's wedding. This was a day when poverty was to be forgotten and everyone could appear wealthy and generous – no matter their real means.

People mixed and mingled, flowing in and out of the tent. Easy banter blended with good-humoured jokes. All knew each other, knew each other's pasts and family histories. And now they shared hardships and struggled as pioneers. Warm comradeship flowed and flowered, sometimes, admittedly aided by a little of the product of the brewer's art – not all of which had travelled from the commercial beer makers in Napier or Palmerston North. Back in Odalen, these people had lived on isolated farmlets. This togetherness, this sense of being part of a village community, was new. Events such as this encouraged the forging of closer bonds.

Smørgåsbord and potluck dinners were well known in the rural backcountry of Norway. They led to ease and informality during mealtimes. People moved about and were jovial. Lids were lifted and complimentary comments made about the contents. Some quiet sampling had even taken place before Randi, and her two pot lids, appeared. She banged them together and called for silence.

Randi was amazed at her own boldness. Here she was, at the centre of a large gathering. She was calling for attention, and was on the point of saying grace, and inviting the multitude to the table . . . And she was not even afraid. She could never, ever, have done that back in Odalen. Her voice was strong and clear as she started on the old grace from her childhood. She half sang, and half chanted: *I Jesu navn går vi til bords . . .**

Then, finally, came the word they had all been waiting for: *Værsågod*†. Indeed, it worked like magic. Like waves

---

* 'In the name of Jesus we go to the table.'
† 'Please accept.'

surging in the same direction, the guests descended upon the groaning tables. Of course, they held back a little here and there, to show they were not over-eager. Still, there was no doubt as to their general direction.

There were no speeches during the long slow meal. Groups formed and reformed. Some by the tables, some seated on the ground outside, everything in a slow state of flux. Johanna and Christian were the only ones seated in one place, and everyone found time to approach them to say a few words and wish them well.

Dusk descended slowly, and the hills lost their shape. There was, as yet, no talk of clearing the tables, or of who would play the piano accordion, or dance, or who would sing a song. One formal item remained before frivolities could be considered. Someone must say: *Takk for maten* – to thank the hostess for the meal. Although everyone had contributed, the words must be directed at Randi.

Ole Olsen, blacksmith and Randi's son-in-law, had not shown his usual healthy appetite during the meal. He knew he had the honour of saying *Takk for maten*, and to add a few well-chosen words. This doubtful honour had bothered him for days. It had given him palpitations and had certainly taken the edge off his appetite. He rose slowly to his feet. Below were a sea of faces, all with their eyes wide open and full of mirth and curiosity. He was known for his booming voice, but that was not enough today. What sort of speechmaker would he be? A hushed silence had settled on the audience.

Throwing caution to the winds, Ole got through the first formal part using his customary loud voice. That was easy enough. No one giggled or smirked. They even looked interested, and Randi was pleased. That was easy to see. Ole's voice gave away the fact that he was intoxicated by his own words. It was strong stuff. He felt full of confidence. Now, for the more daring part of his speech. He launched forth, before fear could overcome him

'Had never tasted so many dishes . . . Had looked forward

to this for days . . . Bit of a cook himself . . . Knew his spices and his condiments . . . Necessary to shoulder his wife aside at times . . .'

Berte Maria was aghast – the cheek of the man! Never did a scrap of work in her kitchen! Oh, she would deal with him later!

However, Ole was in full flight, spurred on by all the titters and the smiles. The audience was clearly in the palm of his hand and he could now safely lower his voice. He had a secret to tell them, several secrets in fact. It was almost in a whisper that he confided to his audience there were more weddings coming up. Quite soon. He could name a few girls straightaway, but better not since he had promised not to divulge. More banquets in the offing – wonderful dishes once more – possibly before Easter – best time to get married – could be warmly recommended. He would bring his own favourite dish as well – Odalen Irish Stew, a secret recipe from his secretive grandmother, bless her. After much rambling and gaiety, he concluded with sensible advice for his listeners. Perhaps they should gently starve themselves in anticipation of the next feast – just as he had done this time. It had sharpened his appetite and added to his enjoyment of Randi's dishes.

Oh, the liar! Just you wait! Even so, Berte Maria smiled indulgently.

The tables had been cleared and a wheezy, hesitant piano accordion could be heard as the bridal couple left the gathering. Johan would drive them to their cottage. He had borrowed the storekeeper's horse and Friberg's buggy. Oh, that buggy! It was Johan's pride and joy. He had built it in early 1874 in his own workshop – the combined smithy and carpenter's place in Lower Norsewood. And it was their first piece of work. Friberg had been so impressed he purchased it even before it was completed. The wheels were larger than usual, and the spokes, though conventional-looking, were made of kanuka. Johan and Ole were proud of their invention.

Soon after that, Johan and Ole had adapted another type of wheel to include New Zealand timber. This one suited low, heavy, box-like little farm carts just like their cart had been back at Pasotorpet. Their first 'economy wheels for poor Norsewood farmers' were merely circles of timber finished with an iron rim. However, their new four-spoked wheels were soon to catch the imagination of Norsewood's cart-owning public. And of course the bumps and jolts endured in the unsprung little carts were another not so gentle reminder of 'home.'

The short trip to the farm opposite Friberg Road had been a romantic journey. Crickets, cicadas and the light breeze whispering in the trees bordering the road, had serenaded them throughout the trip. Johan had turned the buggy around at their gate and wished them goodnight. Johanna and Christian had not spoken since leaving the party. They just held hands, conscious of their beating hearts and every fibre in their bodies quivering. At long last, their own gate, their own house, their own bed.

When she looked back to her wedding night, Johanna could only smile. How innocent she had been, they had both been – and what was all this about sinful thoughts and action? What nonsense! She had enjoyed their play, their exploring, and their games of love from the beginning. It was a gift to them from God. How could that be wrong? Their games got better as they discussed their feelings. How she longed for him when he was at work far away. Those feelings were given words when he returned and they were close together in the big bed with little time for sleep.

8 The entrepreneurs

JOHANNA looked forward to her Wednesday evenings. They had become the high point of her week – unless Christian was at home. She had initiated the English classes herself, and they had grown in popularity among the women, both young and not so young. All very much appreciated getting together, and much more was discussed than just English phrases and sayings. Wednesday 'classes' were the time for airing and discussing whatever issues nagged or annoyed them. Fears, frustration, family tensions, misunderstandings, prejudices, anger . . . there was no end to the personal problems that saw the light of day. They trusted each other. They supported each other. They listened and talked in a spirit of helpfulness. In this atmosphere, few found it difficult to disclose their dark secrets. The women of Norsewood had become a close-knit group.

Fear of the future was the recurring theme. Would the men find work? Close to home? With proper pay? Would they ever be able to clear the land fully and start farming in earnest? Real farming – the sort they had come for. Not just farming grass for grass seed. The problem defied solutions.

They could not solve it no matter how much they talked. And the same conclusion was reached every time. We have to remain optimistic. Without hope and optimism, we will get nowhere.

The women took turns to host the meetings. The hostess was responsible for hot water, and tea and sugar – if they were available. The guests brought something home-baked – but we are not to compete, was the rule. That was after Martha Christoffersen had brought her famous sponge cake, baked in a kerosene tin and cut in two lengthwise. Her sponges were unsurpassable. You could not compete with that! Just plain food from now on please.

They also brought their 'Norsewood Lanterns'. These were obtainable from Ole Olsen's smithy for tuppence each. In fact, they were bottles turned upside down, with the bottoms taken off with hot metal wire. This was where the blacksmith came in. Then a candle was thrust into the necks of the bottles. With the flame sheltered from the wind, the lamps gave very good light. The women, walking together along the bush-lined tracks, felt safe holding the necks of their bottles. Meanwhile the shadows from the candles danced among the trees.

Randi would have nothing to do with the language courses. 'I'll speak Norwegian to my dying day. No members of my family will enter my house and babble away in that strange language.' There was no point in arguing with her. She had made up her mind and that was that.

'Now, look at my little Julius. Fluent and faultless Norwegian, the proper dialect too. He will know where he came from, he will know his roots. I hope you young mothers will do some thinking and not let the language die with you!'

Mother was right, of course, in one way at least. Johanna felt she was caught in a cleft stick. There was loyalty to Mother on one hand, and wasn't Randi just practising what Old Paso had urged them to do before they left Norway? Surely, though, there was another side to this language coin. They were here for good now, whether they wanted it or not.

'We must learn their language,' Johanna kept saying. 'Mix with the locals and talk with them. Our children will marry them and what will become of us then? Outsiders! That will be the case. Feeling increasingly isolated and lonely the older we get.' There were smiles, nods and agreement when she spoke like that. Dear Johanna. She always gave encouragement and set her sights high.

'We are from Odalen, we girls. We can manage anything. Hold onto our language. Hold onto the best from home and learn a new language at the same time. That's us.' The women nodded and smiled, with renewed strength shining from their eyes.

It was good in many ways that Randi had taken such a stand. It meant there was a babysitter available whenever the language classes were on. After Randi had moved back to Norsewood, she and Julius would appear at Garfield every Wednesday afternoon, regular as clockwork. Then they would spend the night there before heading home the next morning.

'That's the least I can do for you,' she would say. 'Don't forget that I want to keep in touch with my grandchildren. And to make sure they learn the proper Odalen dialect,' she added with a smile. Bless those Wednesday afternoons. They cleansed Johanna's soul and gave her a sense of freedom. Bless Randi too for being so helpful.

The language course had received an unexpected boost from Erik Friberg. He had been an enthusiastic supporter before his life was cut short.

'Look,' he had said to Johanna when he'd heard of her plans. 'Here are copies of our latest newspapers. That's the *Wanganui Chronicle*, that one's the *Hawke's Bay Herald*, and here we have the *Manawatu Times*. Take them with you. Read a little aloud in class, and make them repeat. Just a few words. Try it out at home first, but don't let them translate before they have got the sound right . . .' Oh, he was a bit of a bore, that Friberg – and adopting such headmasterly manners. A little annoying, but he meant well.

'Bring them back though. I file them you see. For the Government, that is. But I can always lend you new ones. Good for your pupils to get some news too. To learn what is happening in the Colony.' Friberg slipped easily from a headmaster's attitude to father figure.

Slates and slate pencils had been obtained from the school, as the likeable Mr Thompson was fully in favour of a little adult education. He had come to Norsewood when the school opened in June 1873, and had faced many difficulties. In the classroom, his shy young scholars preferred to say nothing. But the moment they were out in the playground, they exploded into strange noises. Perhaps the children's homework could be set so that mothers and children did it together? A great idea! Young Mr Thompson was all smiles when he handed over six slates and a paper bag containing the slate pencils.

'I wish you success. I do indeed.'

'I wish you success. I do indeed.' These became the opening words of Johanna's first lesson. 'Now say it again. Once more. Again please. And what does it mean? Did you get that?' Johanna had put on a stern schoolmarm expression. They had gathered at Berte Maria's cottage, next door to the smithy at Lower Norsewood.

'That's what he said to me. Mr Thompson. He's so nice – he thinks we will be very helpful to our children.'

There were serious discussions too. And times when tempers flared, as occurred when they were at Karen's place (Karen from Ullerlien). It was a report in the *Wanganui Chronicle* of 15 August 1874 that sparked it off. The article said 'FATAL ACCIDENT – A young Norwegian boy, Valdemar Mortensen, drowned together with eleven bullocks in an attempt to cross the Waipawa River. The station manager, V. Hitchings Esq. has suffered a considerable loss, not just his prize cattle, but also provisions to the value of . . .'

That was the end of the language lesson. The women all knew about accidents. They lived with them daily. Lost in the bush, crushed by a falling tree, swept away in a rain-swollen river, bulls that behaved badly, the axe that slipped… There were many accidents and incidents to be lamented, but Berte Maria brought them quickly back to the Waipawa River.

'He was such a lovely boy, Valdemar, only 15 years old and so proud of his job as a bullock driver. He had used that fording place before. It had been perfectly safe then, but now of course the river was in flood. He had even been told not to attempt the crossing this time, but the over-confident lad ignored the instruction . . .'

It appeared that Berte Maria knew Mr and Mrs Mortensen well. They had had the special wheels – which some people had christened 'Scandi wheels' – fitted to their cart, and had been in for coffee more than once. The formidable Mrs Mortensen had been so proud of her boy. Such a fine looking and capable boy. Good with cattle too. Could turn his hand to any job. Oh yes, no doubt about it, he had been the apple of his mother's eye. Berte Maria was angry. The more she spoke, the angrier she got.

The *Wanganui Chronicle* was several years old when they came across the article about poor Valdemar, and the Norsewood women knew everything about the sad incident. It must have festered in Berte Maria's mind all this time.

'That Mr Hitching! He must have known the river was in flood when he sent Valdemar out on that trip. What was the hurry about? The bullocks could have waited a day or two. And to employ a young boy for such dangerous work! It's a crime. Nothing less. Did he offer any compensation? Not a penny! He didn't even go to see the Mortensens. Didn't even say sorry. What do you think of that?'

Her voice broke. She used a corner of her apron to attend to her eyes – and looked away. The women sat stony-faced.

They had been through this emotional turmoil before, and their thoughts wandered a little. It could so easily have been one of theirs, my Karl, my Knut, my Arne, my Kristoffer . . . Where did he work today? Is he safe this evening? Berte Maria had recovered a little. Anger smouldered and flared again. This time it was vented on the *Wanganui Chronicle*.

'How dare they write like that! Valdemar is hardly mentioned. Is he just one of the bullocks? This newspaper article is mainly about Mr Hitchings and his financial losses. Poor man. How he suffered. That editor has his values all wrong. Is it because we are poor that they treat us like that? Just of no importance? Or is it because we speak a different language?'

Hardly a word was spoken during supper. Johanna tried to think of something cheerful to say to her friends, but failed. There was neither tea nor coffee left in the Olsens' household. Weak kawakawa brew was served with the waffles, pikelets and muffins. There had been manuka tea at the Ericksens' last Wednesday. The women lit their candles, gripped the necks of their upturned bottles and left in silence. The bush was darker than ever. There was nothing cheerful about the dancing shadows tonight. They were just sinister-looking. We might get you one night they seemed to be saying. Where is a spare hand? The women anxiously tried to hold onto one another.

Johanna was terrified of losing a child in the bush. In fact it haunted her, especially after that incident with little Carl August. He was such an intrepid explorer. She had been down by the stream washing clothes, only 200 metres away. When she sensed something was not right, she had abandoned everything in a heap by the creek bed – soap, clean and dirty washing. She wiped her hands on her apron and hastily scrambled up the bank. Her heart beat quickly as she ran through the bush gasping for air. The cottage door was wide open . . .

She had closed it firmly when she left with the washing,

having first told Rangna to keep Carl August inside. Johan was there, still sleeping peacefully in his cot. But the other two? Her heart raced, blood rushed to her head and panic rose within her. Thank God, she found Rangna just behind the cottage. The little mite was crying, and clearly upset. She was pointing towards the bush repeating 'Cal, gone away.'

Oh, what a relief! She found the little explorer just inside the bush. He had not gone very far, but he had given her such a shock. She blamed herself for having been careless, thoughtless, and a poor mother. Even now, months later, she could relive the episode and feel the weight of fear and guilt. Rangna was naturally timid and held Johanna's hand when they went to milk the cows. With Carl August, it was a different matter. He had to come too, but he – and not the cows – was now tethered during milking times. I just can't trust him, Johanna said to herself. The moment I take my eyes off him . . .

She thoroughly understood how two other mothers felt when their boys went missing. They lived on the German Line, close to the Te Whiti Crossing, and had gone down to the river to catch eels. Such adventurous little chaps they were, both only 8 years old. Too adventurous obviously, as they failed to come home before dark. Norsewood was in an uproar. Search parties were sent out into the dark, armed with lanterns and a little food. The search up and down the riverbank went on all night, but to no avail. They found the hinaki eel trap belonging to Herr Schmidt, but no sign of the boys or their catch. A long night became day and more volunteers joined the search – followed by another dark and fruitless night. It was dawn on the second morning before crying was heard. The two wet, scared and very hungry boys were soon found, far from the river and deep in the world of Tane, the forest god. What rejoicing! The searchers were presented with a dozen eggs each.

❋

Eggs! That reminded her. Johanna really had too many eggs these days. Too many potatoes, too much milk, too much butter, cheeses her family would never be able to eat or give away . . . She looked at her place opposite Friberg Road as a small farm these days. When her kahikatea butter box was full, she would go to the shopkeeper at Norsewood.

Mr Drower did not pay well, and cash never changed hands. For every pound of butter Johanna handed over, she could claim four pence worth of goods from the shop. There wasn't much to choose from in Mr Drower's shop, and everything seemed to be on the expensive side. She never felt pleased with herself when she returned home from her bartering expedition with a little brown sugar, a little salt, some flour and occasionally a little tea or coffee. A handful of this and that, Mr Drower said. But he seemed to have rather small hands when it came to tea and coffee. The men had cash when they came home from work, and only then did there seem to be a better selection in the shop. Were things cheaper too? Surely there must be a better business system than just the swapping of goods? And could they take their wares to a place where they might be better appreciated?

These questions had come up in 'English lessons' more than once. What would they have done at home, back in Odalen, under the circumstances? Would they have gone to the local storekeeper with their wares? No. They would have set up a market where people lived, in a village. Gone all the way to Skarnes perhaps. It was Auntie Karen, Karen Christof-fersen, Johan's younger sister who cut the Gordian knot.

'Makaretu is too small. Makotuku and Ormondville? No, not much better. What if we borrow a horse and a cart, a dray? No, a wagon.' Things got bigger and more adventurous in her excitement. 'Load it up. Load it up with everyone's goods for sale and drive to Dannevirke.' There had been a moment of silence. The silence of astonishment. It was all so simple. Why had they not thought of it before? Oh, the laughter and giggles that broke out. They were suddenly a bunch of giggly young girls. All talking at once, and voices drowning out voices.

'Must start early. Before the sun gets up. My hens . . .'

'The cabbages I shall get rid of! Thank goodness.'

'How many should we be? Three? Four?'

'Two rows of early potatoes . . . Hurrah!'

'A bookkeeper is needed. How else can . . .'

'In uniform? Sunday best . . . must look the part.'

'How should I pack my eggs?' Johanna wondered.

Some semblance of order was restored when Karen clapped her hands together and raised her voice above everyone else's.

'Now, now girls. Just listen for a minute. I believe there are very few cows in Dannevirke, very few small farmers in fact. They have huge farms nearby at Tahoraiti and Oringi that are filled with sheep and beef cattle and all that, but are short of all the things we have too much of. Perhaps . . .' She was in full control. All eyes were turned on her. A few quick suggestions to be made before pandemonium broke loose again and the girls tore off on different tangents again.

'We don't want more than three on this expedition.'

'Since I am the oldest one here . . .'

'Hmm . . .'

'No! Since I have the most experience with horses, perhaps I should go.'

There were nods of consent.

'Then there is transport. You know that Ole Blacksmith Olsen has just finished making a new big cart. It's up for sale too. Perhaps he would like to show it off in Dannevirke? Would you like to ask your husband, Berte Maria?' Oh, our Karen was so clever and diplomatic. So decisive too. Next, there would be the question of a horse. Who would handle that? But our decisive Karen was off on a different tack.

'There will be a lot of talking to be done in Dannevirke, explaining who we are and what we are there for and all that. Odalen dialect won't do. No, we need someone who is good at English. We need Johanna – don't you think?' Yes, they all thought so.

'Perhaps, you then, Johanna, would be good enough to go to Mr Drower and ask if we may borrow his horse for the day? It's such a lovely horse too. Could find its own way to Dannevirke. And of course, you know him well.' It was impossible to protest. Karen was so persuasive – and logical – about everything.

'Our Big Day? Should we say 22 December? The day before *Lille Julaften* – when people are shopping for Christmas?' The day seemed to have suited everyone, Johanna as well, but her thoughts were on *Lille Julaften* seven years earlier.

True, Ole Olsen had built a new big cart he was extremely proud of. It had a padded seat wide enough for three people, and its seat was also nicely sprung. Most useful, the women knew only too well, for travelling long distances in a cart fitted with the so-called 'Scandi wheels'. 'Scandi wagons' were very good for heavy loads, but they did not ordinarily cater to the comfort of their drivers. And, of course, Ole was looking for a buyer, so he did want his new creation to be seen. Berte Maria had no difficulty obtaining the use of it for the day.

It proved just as easy to borrow the horse. Mr Drower had been all smiles and kindness. No, he did not see it as competition. Certainly not. To be honest, he had difficulties disposing of all the eggs, butter, etc., etc., that came to his shop. It was a splendid idea on the part of the ladies, to look for another outlet for their produce. Very sound business indeed. He wished them every success. A pleasure to lend them the horse. Oh, yes, free of charge this time, but in the future? Perhaps some small fee, acceptable to all concerned.

Mr Drower was indeed pleased to have a pause in all this butter, cheese and egg trade. Nowadays he sent most of it on to his other store at Waipukurau, or to Napier or Hastings, but freight was unreliable, and some things could not cope with hot Hawke's Bay temperatures or accidental delays on railway sidings – and prices fluctuated. And, of course, the butter could at times – to be honest – be a little rancid. Just a little! If the women could sell their blessed butter in Dannevirke . . . then they would come back with cash in their pockets. Proper coins and better still, crisp bank notes. Now that would be better.

The horse was delivered at Lower Norsewood on Tuesday 21 December and Berte Maria seemed to have been busy with her pencil and paper most of the day:

From Martha K: two bags of carrots, one bag of cauliflowers, six cheeses (in box), six hens (alive, box).

From Martha J: one bag of early potatoes, one bag of cabbages, three dozen eggs, one bag of onions, one box butter, one box cheeses.

From Ellen O . . . from Anne J . . . from Karen U . . . from Karen L . . . It had gone on all afternoon and well into the evening. Ole had been very helpful, bless him. He had loaded up the cart, albeit ever so carefully, to avoid scratching the paintwork. He had stacked and organised, made sure the poor hens had air, and the cheeses were not squashed. He also made sure the boxes, cases, bags and parcels were securely closed and labelled. What a business, but what a jovial atmosphere and such an air of optimism and happy anticipation. Berte Maria had been quite bossy.

'Here's a spare pencil. You label your own boxes, won't you? Please – let me taste that butter. A bit on the salty side, don't you think? Those cheeses, no. They are too fresh. Only two days old if you ask me. No, not tomorrow, next time.' Thank goodness there was coffee in the house and their oldest daughter, Marthea, now 16 years old, had made herself useful for once. What had come over the girl? She was normally so difficult. Would be cheeky to her mother, answer back and oppose everything. And moody too, and sulky. Now, today, she had baked good yeast buns – yeast buns with raisins in them – and every bit as good as those Randi could produce. Moreover, she served coffee, smiled and chattered easily with the callers as they came. Anyone would think she was the hostess. Well, long may it last. Let's hope she's not getting ideas above her station in life. She is not trying to impress that Andersen boy by any chance? The one who was helping his mother with all those onions, and who was hanging around for so long. It was amazing how long onions could take.

The overloaded cart left just before daybreak. The horse strained to drag it up the small hill out of Lower Norsewood. It was obvious the three commercial travellers had discussed what to wear. Anyone would think they had settled on an eye-catching uniform, red kerchiefs for all three, black ankle-length skirts, white blouses and black shawls over their shoulders in the cool morning air. They looked splendid, just splendid. Many of their suppliers had seen them off, and were loud in their encouragement.

'Best of luck.'

'Look out for highwaymen.'

'Safe journey. Come back with full pockets and an empty cart.'

Voices were soon lost with the turning of wheels in the morning air.

It was not yet six a. m. With luck they would be there by nine, and with further luck would have everything sold by early afternoon. A nice shady place was needed, as it was going to be a hot day. Perhaps that little park on the left side of the main street . . . How would they attract people's attention? The three were now a mixture of happy anticipation and anxiety. It was good to talk. Talk, joke and laugh in an attempt to dispel some of the tension they all felt. The road was good. Downhill most of the way – and straightened out and repaired after the huge flood last March. Two bridges had been swept away, not to mention all the gravel.

Roadwork, gravel, repairs, shovel, pick, axe and wheel-barrow. Johanna had entered her inner world again. Christian would be home tomorrow, Friday at the very latest – but that was Christmas Eve! Did his boss know how important 24 December was? That it was *Julaften* itself? The most sacred day of the year!

You should be home in time for that. Before that! How pleased he would be if she had money to show him. And it would be his money. All of it. She had to make that clear – since everything had come off his farm. Yes, we can call it a farm from now on. Would he miss the hens? They had stopped laying, were getting too old. Christian would understand. He understood everything. Would he pick her up? Swing her in the air until she felt delightfully dizzy and light-headed? Give her one of those kisses that said so much and promised even more?

It was getting hot. The shawls had come off their shoulders. Poupoutua Peak trembled in the morning haze. They stopped at the Manga-te-wai-iti, drank from the cool stream, and let Hercules the horse have his fill. It was a shady, restful place, still with dew on the ground. Karen's stale waffles with salty butter tasted wonderful. A sense of urgency had come over them though. They walked up the hill, beside the horse, to lighten his load. They were to do the same thing an hour later after crossing the Mangatera.

Could news about Three Ladies and a Horse – as they had jokingly called themselves – have reached Dannevirke ahead of them? It seemed almost as if they were expected. They had hardly reached their little wayside park before potential customers were there – some just to gaze and gawk admittedly. Most, though, had coins clanking in their apron pockets, such sweet music. Not only women gathered, far from it. Gentlemen appeared from nowhere. It was quite a miracle how they could materialise out of nowhere. Some made themselves useful as well when it came to handling boxes and bags.

The Three Ladies were grateful for any help, and made that clear. They were rather eye-catching in their colourful attire, all in red, white and black. Good looking too. A little dusty, that could not be denied, but still resplendent. They were agile and cheerful, filled with smiles, good humoured, and with easy banter in Odalen dialect as well as English. It was a true pleasure to help them with bags and boxes.

Business was brisk. Early potatoes, onions, carrots, not to mention eggs, cheeses and butter . . . all had gone before twelve noon.

'Hens? Are they laying?'

'Not yet. Soon, just moulting these days. Won't be long though.' The poor, faithful hens, always so cheerful around the house with their clucking noises. Would the new owners keep them, or would they end up in the pot? On the Christmas table perhaps? The last sack of potatoes went for sixpence to a Danish storekeeper. Much too cheap, but they wanted a quick sale and then away. There was no harm in appearing generous at the end, and to let the buyer think he had a bargain.

They were off. 'We'll be back after the New Year,' was the cheerful adieu. '*E noho ra.*' Johanna was proud of the few Maori words she had mastered. She pronounced each letter separately and with her open, clear vowels from Odalen.

Berte Maria had been busy with pencil and paper the whole time the business transactions went on. She had stumbled mentally once or twice, and had mixed up her two Karens and the two Marthas, but was nearing the end of her bookkeeping. It had been a gruelling task to put the right sale price beside each item, and to match it with the right owner. Still, it was all going to look very nice and correct in the end. Itemised first, then:

> *Martha K. 12 shillings and 4$^{1}/_{2}$ pence*
> *Martha J. 22 shillings and 6$^{1}/_{2}$ pence*

Nice and tidy, and not a penny left over in the end.

Nothing extra for the Three Ladies and their Horse? That would not be right.

They rested at the Manga-te-wai-nui, washed their faces in the heavenly cool water, and drank from cupped hands. Hercules the horse also seemed thankful for a spell. Even so, he knew he was close to home . . . so let us be going.

The Ruahine Ranges were in hues of deep green. Cumulus clouds were building up behind them, and spilling over the skyline. A peaceful and ancient landscape still lay to their left, but everything lay broken and disturbed to their right.

Christian would be home tomorrow. Peace and ancient rituals ahead – never mind if broken, turbulent times might follow.

Karen was pleased with herself. She had handled the horse without difficulties. And no one knew how apprehensive she had been about the whole Herculean adventure.

Berte Maria was ecstatic: 'We are rich, girls. Rich! We should buy this cart from Ole! I've learnt how to haggle about prices.' Her calculations were finished at last. Sums all correct, checked and double-checked – and no one knew her mathematical skills had been tested to the full this Wednesday, 22 December.

9 The great flood

In the 1960s, the Ministry of Works, in its eagerness to improve State Highway 2, cut Norsewood in two. This left both parts high (or in one case 'low') and dry. True, there had always been two parts to Norsewood, 'Upper' and 'Lower'. However, the Napier-Manawatu highway that snaked its way between the pair also held them together.

When you enter Norsewood today, you enter the past. You enter history. The whole place, so it seemed to me, is like a living museum. The street names point back to Norway: Thor Street, Eric Street, Viking Street, Eriksen Street and several others. The exception is the main street (an extension of Eric Street) that bears the incongruous name of Coronation Street. This street honours the 1902 coronation of an English king (albeit half-German) and his Danish-born Queen.

Time can seem to have stood still at Norsewood. The town never graduated beyond the scale of a large village. A vague tradition claims the railway was once going to pass through Norsewood. This is despite the town, at 388 metres above sea level, being the highest point on the Hawke's Bay road route. Instead, the railway was built through nearby Ormondville, which is at a much lower elevation, only 300 metres above sea level.

Because of this, Ormondville gained the governmental infra-structure Norsewood craved. It retained this status during the many decades that the iron horse predominated. Since that time, though, the position of local dominance has largely reversed.

The surveyed route also planned to bypass Dannevirke, but in the end the potential cost rendered the original route too expensive. Even so, the main railway station was built at Tahoraiti (then spelt Tahoraite) to suit wealthy sheep farmers and sawmillers, who were based nearby. Later it was relocated to Dannevirke when that town suddenly came to life. Dannevirke, originally far smaller and even more remote than Norsewood, grew to become the district's principal town.

Norsewood's locals are no longer upset by their town's reduced status. When they gather at the Crown Hotel every Thursday evening, they are like a big family. Everyone knows everyone else and they look after each other. 'Look at the towns,' they say. 'All the violence and criminality. We have nothing like that, thank goodness, because we are so few and know each other.'

Hansen and Olsen, Magnussen and Mortensen, Andersen and Gundersen – the names again point back to Norway. They are farmers or shearers, or they work at 'Norsewear', the big clothing factory started by the late Ole Rian, from Orkanger, near Trondheim, in the 1960s.

The present Crown Hotel, built to replace the original that burnt down in 1916, looks much the same, inside and out, as it did when new. There are signs of a picture theatre and a hall at the far end of Coronation Street. Here frivolous activities may have taken place – but to balance this, at the other end of the street stood the Salvation Army Church. It may be decades since any stirring music was heard from this building, but the name is still clearly visible on walls that cry out for a coat of paint. I have been told that in its heyday, Norsewood boasted seven churches.

Coronation Street has always been a meeting place, today as well as over a hundred years ago. I have walked up and down this street many times, and have sensed the footsteps of my compatriots. Here, Christian walked as a young man – and as an old man. This was the place for news to be exchanged, as was the case with the unemployed at Christmas time in 1880.

Christian was not only amazed, he was delighted. Thirty shillings and four pence! It was more than he could earn in a whole week. What a girl! What a wife he had! What a Christmas present to come home to.

He could hardly believe his eyes when Johanna fetched the tin – oh, it seemed so heavy – from the corner cupboard. It was music to his ear when she turned it upside down on the table. Shiny silver coins had rolled out among all the big brown pennies – like a few queens among an army of peasants. Perhaps it said something about the economic strength of the well-heeled community that lived just beyond Dannevirke. Christian threw his hands up in the air.

'Johanna, you are top of the class! Best girl in the whole Hawke's Bay. How did you do it? Come and sit here, on my lap, and tell me all about it.' There were hugs and kisses, as Johanna poured out the whole exciting story.

'And we plan to do it again. The Three Ladies and a Horse. I mean, after the New Year. Would you believe it Christian? I felt just like a lady yesterday. So rich and free, and not a care in the world. That's what a lady feels, don't you think?'

The serious-looking little Rangna, and the ever lively Carl August, wanted to be in on the hilarity too, and also found a place on Christian's knee. What was that stain in the corner of his mouth? Johanna had not seen that before.

'You have stopped smoking, haven't you? You promised that when we married. Thrown your pipe away for good, you said?'

'Oh yes, for good and ever. Just chew a little tobacco from time to time. Just a little.' Christian looked uneasy and studied the tips of his boots.

'It's just your health that I'm concerned about. There are so many men coughing these days, and they all seem to be smoking. Or they chew the tobacco and spit it out everywhere. Tobacco is dangerous – and spitting it everywhere is disgusting! Christian, did you hear that? It is simply . . .'

Suddenly Johanna was overcome by a coughing fit herself. She quickly extracted herself from Christian's knee, and stood hunched over, hands clasping her chest. It was a deep, long-drawn, raking cough. Tears ran, her face reddened, yet still she tried to joke when she finally looked up.

'No, I haven't taken over your pipe. It's just that I've had a cold lately. Summer colds, you know, are always difficult to shake off.' She did not refer to what she feared the most. What her father, Eric Friberg and so many others had died of. However, when Christian looked hard at her, she seemed a little thinner than last time he was home. Her cheeks did not seem so full and she had been so light when he had picked her up and swung her in the air.

'You are not seriously ill? You mustn't be! You are not allowed to be!' His voice was loud – and trembled as it sank an octave or two.

'We must get a doctor, Johanna! To examine both you and Rangna. Our little girl does not look at all well.' He stroked Rangna's hair gently. Johanna followed his hand, her eyes conveying deep concern.

'It's not serious with me, Christian. Mine is just a stubborn cold. It will pass soon. But Rangna needs to see a doctor. She has been poorly for so long.' She placed her hand on the child's forehead.

'Feels hot again. Feverish I fear. On and off now for days. Most evenings anyway,' she added.

Finding a doctor was easier said than done. Neither Norsewood nor Dannevirke had one, and Dr Green from Napier was not keen on visits to the Seventy-Mile-Bush. The 'Scandies' were not known for their ready money either – especially now that work had become scarce.

The joy of homecoming had faded for Christian. Health problems were one thing, but he had something else on his mind as well. A heavy load. Perhaps he should share it with Johanna straightaway.

'I have lost my job. Our whole gang was fired. No more contracts to be had,' the boss said, 'Stay home after Christmas.' Christian went on to explain that they were working south of Woodville, and had hoped to start in the Manawatu Gorge in the New Year. Too far from home, the supervisor had said. Preference had to be given to local gangs. The struggling English immigrants from Woodville needed work too.

The employment situation was bad, but health problems were worse. How could he face the future if the worst occurred? Without her, life in New Zealand had no meaning. Christian saw himself as a widower with three small children, no income, and no support of any kind. He shuddered when he looked into that black abyss.

Johanna must have read his thoughts. 'We'll get by Christian. Now you have time to clear and burn all those trees you felled last winter. Then we can have more paddocks. Like a proper farm. Like you have always wanted. And we can grow more vegetables. Dannevirke can take whatever we grow.' She could not bear to see her husband so down-hearted. 'I'm not sick. This cough will soon pass.'

Christian felt a little easier. Dear Johanna, bless her. Always so optimistic and positive. Even so, fear gnawed at his heart. He prayed inwardly, but courage and optimism would not be enough if real illness struck. Please God, let her be alright. Let Johanna be alright.

'I'll look for some other work. People tell me that the sawmill that Mrs Friberg is having built on her farm at Makotuku will be starting soon. It will be needing workers in the bush as well as at the sawmill. And Mrs Friberg deserves trustworthy people. It takes a very brave woman to start such a business, and she could get into strife very easily. Still, she has decided to take the risk and the trees are hers to mill.'

Christian was smiling again. 'I'll find out during Christmas for sure. After all, I'm a bushman, a man of the forest really. Not a road worker. And if I get the job, then – no more tobacco. I promise, the future is ours still.'

In spite of that and in spite of the warmth and intimacy they both longed for, Christian could not sleep that night.

The future is ours. How many times had he said that before? And how many times had he been disappointed? He was facing only defeats, each defeat following the one before. Work on the road, work on the railway, and then back to the road. Nothing solid, nothing lasting, and never enough income to meet the future. He should have added to the house by now. He should have had a sturdy draught horse to help him clear the land. There should have been proper paddocks to plough, to sow and to harvest. Not just miserable little pockets of land. Dreams. Dreams about the future. Dreams without substance. Why couldn't at least some of his dreams be realised?

His workmates were no better off. Worse if anything. They were all trapped in this economic bog – and despairing of ever making it to the other side. Some had resigned all hope and spoken of God and His mysterious ways. Still, Christian would have none of that. Defeatist attitudes were harmful. No, they were not for him.

'Not me. Not me!' Johanna woke up with a shock. Her husband was sitting on the edge of their bed, waving his arms in the air. She threw her arms around his neck and pulled him back into bed.

'Oh, Christian dear, a bad nightmare was it?'

No, not a real dream. Not the sort she thought. He wanted to explain, but it was all so disjointed. She stroked his hair slowly, slowly – calming him down.

'Don't think about it. So many good things have happened to us. And we have twenty-seven sheep, two cows, a yearling and two calves, a pig, fowls, and land that can produce anything. Sleep now. Let us both go to sleep.' She snuggled closely against him, her arm comfortingly over him. The warmth of her body had a healing effect. Peace descended and soon they slept, locked like young lovers in each other's arms. At least they did until baby Johan awoke and abruptly reminded them it was breakfast time.

Feeling impatient, Christian left early for Norsewood. He was eager to meet with friends and hear the latest news. The sun was already warm in a deep blue sky. Clouds as white as snow drifted from behind the backbone of the Ruahine Ranges. The ranges, in turn, formed a dividing line between the dark green of the bush and the deep blue above. Such light, such clear contrasting colours. Surely that was a sign the future would be brighter. Not dull and grey as it had so often been in the past. It was a joy to fill his lungs with the clean, fresh morning air. Even the smells were good. The flowers, the trees by the roadside, even the dust he stirred up as he walked. He had built this road himself, he and his mates. He knew it was good, like the road to his future.

Johanna was right. They did have land and they did have twenty-seven sheep, two cows, the young stock, a pig and fowls as well. No reason to despair. There were eels in the river and wild pigs in the bush – all free – even if pigs repulsed Johanna. And, of course, there were the Three Ladies and a Horse. What a bonus that had turned out to be! The future looked bright, like nature's colours ahead of him.

He made the journey to Norsewood in record time, the sweat running down his back as he climbed the steep hill to Upper Norsewood. It was Friday and Christmas Eve, and the main street was crowded with people. The school, on his right, was closed for the holidays, but children played in the grounds while a few hens pecked and scratched alongside the fence. The multitudes had gathered outside Mr Drower's General Store. Men only, it seemed, in small groups. Some smoking, some chewing tobacco and occasionally spitting. Some with their hands deep in their empty pockets. Some waving an arm in the air to emphasise some point just made. Still, they had one thing in common. They were all in their Sunday best, for it was, after all, Christmas Eve.

Those fortunate enough to have jobs were there as well, and they seemed to be at the centre of each little group. They would have useful information to pass on regarding future employment opportunities, and listeners were hanging on their every word. Handshaking was occurring on a grand scale, with the familiar *Takk for sist*.[*]

Takk for sist came in return.

Christian recognised Fredrik, his brother-in-law, from a distance. He was deep in conversation with Arne Christiansen, the shoemaker from Vinger[†], who was known for his unkempt appearance as well as his volatile temper. Beside them were the two brothers, Lars and Halvor Larsen. They were slender young boys when they arrived in Norsewood with their widowed mother, Eli Torkelsdatter Ullerlien. But look at them now! Big strong men, whose physical strength had been gained 'squaring' sleepers for the railway, and sometimes laying them as well. Halvor was only 19, while Lars was four years older, but both were married men and that had helped them to obtain work. They talked freely about their jobs, and it was obvious work had given them status and self-esteem. On the topic of marital bliss, though, they were silent.

Arne Shoemaker, as Arne Christiansen was now commonly known, had brought his pig dog of mixed heritage along with him. Caesar was Arne's constant companion, although now he was securely tied to a verandah post on the other side of the street. The dog had been a gift from a Maori workmate at Makotuku, but seemed to have adopted the looks as well as the temperament of his new master. He was well known as a very untidy and unkempt dog that

---

* Literally, 'Thank you for our last meeting', which is said whenever friends meet.
† Arne Christiansen later adopted 'Vinger' as his surname.

snarled and bared his teeth with ease. He was also reputed to be to be a ferocious pig dog, and one that did not always distinguish between pigs and humans.

Christian joined this little group and was welcomed with heavy handshaking and *Takk for sist.* Caesar snarled from the other side of the street, and tugged at his rope, his yellow eyes shooting sparks. Arne, like Caesar, had been busy venting his anger and was not about to be stopped.

'So to hell with Ormond. It's his fault Norsewood is in the doldrums. If we had gotten the railway as promised, we would have been well off today. The Devil take him!'

Caesar snarled encouragement from the verandah post. 'And he had the cheek to have a town named after himself. Ormondville! Have you heard the like!' He brushed aside the fact that the grateful people of Ormondville had chosen the name, and not Ormond himself.

It was not the first time the name of John Davis Ormond had been mentioned in anger. Many years had passed since the decision was made that the railway between Napier and Palmerston North would go south of Norsewood – and not through the settlement as the Scandinavian pioneers had thought. Ormond had bought vast tracts of land between Takapau and Dannevirke as early as 1863. And of course, who could be sure that this Norsewood railway had not been another of Friberg's stories – used to inspire or pacify the immigrants when he deemed such actions necessary?

'Still, Ormond got all that land cheaply, didn't he now. For a song – so the railway would go through his land and make him richer still! Being rich at our expense. That's what it is! Good business sense some people may say. Oh, no. Far from it. Daylight robbery if you ask me.' Arne had not finished yet. It seemed that Caesar from across the street was in full support. He, too, wanted a piece of John Davis Ormond.

'We cleared the land for him. Mean paymaster he was too, and now every acre along that railway line is worth £80.

No justice in that. I'll let Caesar have a go at him one day – if I see him. That will be bloody justice. If we used our brains we would emigrate, the lot of us. Up stakes and away to America, to Australia, or at least well away from Norsewood – just like Elliot Greiner. I'm sure he is better off up in Gisborne than we are here.'

Christian had grown a little tired of the tirades about Ormond. He had heard it all before, more than once, and not only from Arne Shoemaker. No doubt, Ormond had been a successful speculator. However, even he had only known from around 1870 where the surveyor and engineers had thought the railway should go. And it was only logical to go over the flattest possible terrain in this rugged district. Not up into the hills to Norsewood. All this anger seemed so pointless and certainly heated accusations were prone to exaggeration.

He realised that in the six weeks since he was last home, nothing had changed in Norsewood. Back then, everyone had attended a meeting at the school. They had put their signatures on a letter to the Waipawa County Council, demanding work for the jobless. It had all seemed so important. Christian and his workmates in the road gang had even postponed their departure for Woodville a whole day, so they could attend the meeting. They were among the lucky ones, as they had had continuous work since the flood last March. The majority, though, were unemployed – and this was the moment to show solidarity and support.

What a long meeting it had been! News about the meeting had been passed by word of mouth only, yet the schoolroom was packed with people. Absolutely packed. It had been painful to see grown men weep. One by one, they had come forward to tell their tales of hardship and hunger. Some spoke in English, some in Irish-English, some in Odalen-English, and many found it difficult to control their tears. Christian cringed when he saw Anders Olsen from Fredrikstad take the floor.

Anders was Christian's neighbour, and he, with his Christina, had also arrived in 1873. Since then, they had been blessed with four children. As a neighbour, Anders could not be bettered, but as a linguist . . . Oh, no! Nobody could understand him unless they came from Fredrikstad. And so it turned out. Pastor Sass had lifted his arm in defence and the chairman looked bewildered.

Christian wished he could sink through the floor, but he admired the man even so. Courageous chap he was, a daunting task to face a large audience like this. Would I dare to do that? No, not ever. Perhaps, one day . . . if Johanna helped me prepare the speech, and I had time to practise. Perhaps.

It was Hans Pedersen who summed up the mood of the meeting, and he did it so easily; slow and deliberate, never taking his eyes off the chairman.

'I can work hard, but there is no job to be found. Neither easy work nor hard work. The Government told us there would be work for anyone, everyone. It is their job now to find us work. A promise is a promise. Gentlemen cannot go back on their word.'

Hans sat down a little flushed, his heart still racing. It had been a great test of courage to get to his feet, even if he had learned his speech by heart. Now he felt hugely relieved. Everyone had listened attentively. My word! Hans had hit the nail on its head. It was all so simple. Pen, ink and paper had been found and the letter written, admittedly with somewhat long and involved sentences. Still, the general message remained clear. It had taken another hour that night for everyone to sign it.

The letter caused quite a stir. Both the *Hawke's Bay Herald* and the *Waipawa Mail* published lengthy reports on the meeting and the sentiments expressed that Monday evening. They also noted nearly every adult male resident of the settlement had attended. The *Hawke's Bay Herald* went a step further in its article of 11 November 1880. It said many immigrants now sincerely wished to return to their countries of origin. It added that if assistance to the settlers was not forthcoming the chances were they would turn their backs on this country, for which they had worked faithfully for seven or eight years.

And had assistance been forthcoming? Nothing of the sort, Christian concluded. The precious letter, written after so many tears six weeks ago, had brought no results. The same groups of jobless people were still here. Still standing around in the main street outside Drower's store, discussing job prospects, swearing, cursing . . . Yet there was a small ray of hope this time? Was there any real substance to this sawmill at Makotuku? Could Mrs Friberg really achieve what she hoped to do? Women sawmillers were not exactly everyday occurrences! And what Fredrick kept repeating – a small sawmill to open in Norsewood soon? The railway might have bypassed Norsewood, but its influence, as an outlet for the district's timber, was not lost on the district's entrepreneurs.

Vast, untouched forest grew throughout the whole district. True, settlers had been wrestling with the trees on their own properties for years, but this felling had scarcely scratched the surface. Huge areas had never felt the fire, never seen the axe, and never heard the screech of the saw. In his mind's eye, Christian saw the huge trees – ancient, majestic, some like shaggy trolls. A pity to touch them, but thousands of houses are locked up in all that timber. Totara blocks for house piles, for windowsills, joinery . . . rimu for walls, stringers, joists . . . matai for flooring, hard as the hobs of . . . It would have to be a big mill.

More realistically, he knew, it would mean many mills, both big and small. No doubt about it since all that timber was available. It would be there a long time. And that meant steady work, and a steady income, for years to come. A big labour force too. Not just at the mills themselves, but in the separate teams working independently in the bush. Felling their own section and responsible for their own haulage lines perhaps. Tramlines through the bush, even. Road haulage to the railway station, and road repair workers to maintain the roads used constantly by heavy timber wagons.

Many teams and many types of jobs would mean many contracts. Contracts implied a boss, a contractor with his own team. Many good things would result from all this for the struggling settlers and their families. Visions, ideas, calculations, everything flashed through Christian's mind, then returned in a different light, piled up – and stayed there. Could I? Would I dare to?

'The Makotuku mill. It should be a big place. I could apply for a bush contract, get my own men . . .'

It had only been thinking aloud, but Arne had heard it. He understood. Visions of his future floated through his mind as well.

'You can do it, Christian. You are just the type of man Mrs Friberg will be looking for. With your work record too . . . always solid. That's the type of work I would . . . if you should . . . I am never ill either, not a sick day in my life. And Caesar would like to see more of the bush too.' A growl of approval came from the other side of the street. Arne was flushed with new hope and the thought of a steady income. But tact was needed at this stage. Not too pushy, not too eager, or Christian would lose interest in him.

He had said it. Mainly to himself. His thoughts had run away with him, but it was too late to go back on anything. 'I'll do my best, but God knows I shall miss Bror Erik Friberg. He would have been our best helper. And of course his poor widow's best helper in this situation too,' he added slowly.

There was silence. The shoemaker was busy examining the tips of his boots. It was a sore point with him that he had not attended Friberg's funeral almost three years ago. At that time, he still felt angry with the Swede for having misled him, but later he and others began to see things in a different light. Slowly it had dawned on him that while Friberg was the administrator, there had been work for everyone. With his passing things had changed. Jobs became scarce, wages decreased – and no new 'Administrator for Scandinavians' was appointed.

Fredrik felt the tension.

'We lost our real helper that day.'

Arne was not going to give in so easily. Pride was at stake.

'All the lies he told. He lied to us, didn't he?'

'Perhaps someone lied to him. Misled him.'

'Who? What? Friberg misled?'

'Yes, by the Government. And they broke their promise. Anyway, once we were here he did his best for us. No one can deny that! We lost a good man in Bror Erik Friberg! Full stop.'

This did indeed put a stop to the topic. Arne felt he had salvaged some of his honour so further contradictions were not necessary – for the time being.

Christian was lost in his own thoughts. How well he remembered the funeral in February 1878. He remembered standing at the graveside as psalms were sung. He remembered yellow soil, the sun so hot in the blue sky. Cecilia Friberg in her widow's weeds, still straight, dignified and defiant-looking . . . He understood even then that this was a loss the whole of Norsewood would feel. Friberg was well-liked by his superiors and had managed to start so many projects. But when the consumption broke him, his work schemes fell apart as well. So it seemed anyway.

When the railway from Napier had reached Waipawa in 1876, work also seemed to have stopped, at least for some weeks. Was it really Friberg who got things going once more? At least it was he who found work for Christian and his gang. After that, they had laid sleepers all the way to Waipukurau and then on to Takapau. He would forever be thankful to the man.

Ole 'Blacksmith', his brother-in-law, had now joined the group. He had sidled up quietly without his usual fanfare.

He was chewing on something and looking very pleased with himself.

'Berte Maria did the smoking last night, long and slow, all night in the chimney. Room for six in there, used manuka sawdust. Says that is the best. Happy Christmas. Oh, I should have said that first. Would you like a taste?'

So that's what Ole had tucked inside his flax *kit*. Smoked eels! He produced one and peeled it like a banana, his gnarled fingers betraying his profession. Pink and grey and oily it was, and simply delicious-looking. It slipped off the backbone too. Oh Berte Maria, bless you. You are simply an expert. Smiles of deep satisfaction spread on all faces as they chewed slowly, savouring the full flavour as long as possible.

'Keep the rest. There is not much left on him.' And with that Ole and his flax *kit* sidled off to join another group.

Who do we have here? Christian looked at the sad figure of a man working his way ever so slowly along the street. He used a stick. He had a boot on one foot, but the other was bandaged with a sack and the trouser leg rolled up to the knee. The poor pathetic man limped slowly in their direction. Oh, my God! It was Anders Olsen from Fredrikstad. The defender of the poor who had tried to make his point clear at the meeting six weeks ago. My neighbour! In such a state, and in great pain by the look of it. And I didn't know a thing.

Anders reached them finally and tried to smile. There was a lot of explaining to be done. The accident had happened some days ago. He had been trying to bring in a cow for Christine. However, it had bolted into the bush, and then there was a hole in the ground he didn't know was there. Very painful it had been. Christine had found him in the end and had helped him back to the house . . . He had been there ever since, sitting still for ten days, his leg on the milking stool because that's what Christine had told him to do. It had been dreadful.

Doctor?

No, it would heal itself, but today he simply had to get out and see people, and to wish them Happy Christmas. Well, yes, there was one more thing. They were out of flour and Christine had said there would be no proper Christmas without some baking being done. So he was on his way to see Mr Drower. With that, Anders limped off in the direction of the store.

Christian caught up with him just inside the door and out of sight of his friends.

'Do you have money for the flour?'

'Not yet. Drower will extend my credit. It's Christmas you know.'

'Here, take this,' and he pressed two shiny shillings into Anders' hand. Anders was silent. He cleared his throat once or twice, but did not manage to protest. However, his eyes were moist and as shiny as the two coins.

On his way home, Christian sat down in the shade of a matai tree with bark the colour of hammered copper. His last bit of tobacco would taste so good – and with care could last until he got home. He felt light-headed. He felt like Christmas. Two shillings. That's not very much. Only half a day's pay, but enough to buy three pounds of flour, a little tea and sugar, and a handful of raisins. Yet it was the big parcel under his arm that really excited him. She deserved it. Johanna would be so pleased to receive this painting. They had no real pictures at home, just bare wooden walls with a few bits and pieces dangling from them. This one would look extra nice. It was big too – 51 cm by 38 cm, and already framed.

The artist had been a painter's apprentice in Christiania. When he found himself short of work he had turned to painting landscapes and portraits. What he may have lacked in formal training he made up for in earnest endeavour. He tried hard to interpret his subjects, and worked in the spirit of the Impressionists. Johan Stadmo, father of three, had been allowed to use Mr Drower's store as his art gallery. And there it had been with its ticket saying one shilling and sixpence.

Martin Luther, in shades of green and light brown, stared at Christian from the wall. 'Buy me now', he seemed to say. Respectfully tucked in the bottom right-hand corner, in small black lettering, was the artist's name: Stadmo, 1879.

Would Johanna ever get a better Christmas present? She admired Martin Luther as a man of great courage, who had brought Christendom back to Christ. More than once she had reminded Christian to follow the straight and narrow path in life. With Martin Luther's picture on the wall, they would always be reminded of his advice.

People looked on in utter astonishment when he put two shillings on the counter and asked for Martin Luther and the rest in boiled lollies. Despite all the sideways glances, Christian felt elated. With one little reckless action, he seemed to have achieved three things: a little support for the poor painter and his three children; the ideal gift for Johanna; and on top of that a few lollies for his own children. It would be Christmas for Rangna and Carl August too. They were not spoilt when it came to sweet things – and he looked forward to seeing their faces this evening. Perhaps only three lollies each today. Christmas was to be more than just one evening.

Was that the whirring of a saw he heard? From the direction of Lower Norsewood? Or perhaps the mischievous wind had carried the sound from Gundrie's mill at Ormondville? A good omen indeed! No doubt about it. Was that the deeper note of the saw blade meeting hardwood, and being forced to slow down? And was that the screech of dealing with a knot? He knew the music of the circular saw, but listen to that! It was the saw 'running loose,' the high-pitched sound of the operator pulling the plank back. Music to his ears indeed – as sweet as the song of the bellbird and so full of promise. Gundrie's mill was only small fry – on that site anyway. However, Makotuku, that would be the big stuff. Now then, if I can get a contract there, he mused, who should be in my team? Fredrik, of course – the two Larsen brothers for sure, Lars and Halvor, simply because they were such good workers. Arne Shoemaker ought to be there for the sake of his health – mental health that is. He will soon be rather grumpy and despondent without work, and a danger to himself and his family. Who else? It would have to be Anders Olsen with the painful foot next. Anders was so courageous and long-suffering, and he was desperately in need of work and some income for his Christina and their four children.

The tobacco disposed of, Christian scrambled back to his feet and headed off on the last kilometre towards home. How he had run that distance – if from the other direction – last March after the flood!

The road had been a mess then. Washed out here and there, deep in mud in places, and with branches and twigs strewn everywhere. He and some of his fitter companions had run the last leg of the journey back from Tahoraiti. Christian had ignored the rasping pain in his chest and the taste of blood in his mouth. He finally slowed when he saw smoke rising from the chimney. Moments later, he had been overcome with gratitude when he recognised Rangna and Carl August playing outside the house. Meanwhile the hens pecked and scratched contentedly . . . and everything seemed perfectly normal. He had knelt down on the road at that point and thanked God they were alright.

The 1880 flood has been described as the equivalent of Cyclone Bola (March 1988) hitting Southern Hawke's Bay. It remains the Manawatu River's third largest recorded flood, although Southern Hawke's Bay experienced the actual storm – along with Wairarapa, Wellington and the upper South Island.

The storm had scarcely touched the unsuspecting Manawatu district, yet the Manawatu River, sourced near Norsewood, carried the storm's run-off. Having experienced little rain and with minimal flood protection or warning systems, the district suffered massively when the floodwaters overwhelmed it at night.

A 3-year-old girl drowned at Tiakitahuna, below Palmerston North, when a floating log overturned her family's (floating) dray as they tried to escape. Other near tragedies included workmen and Maori villagers at Tahoraiti.

Manawatu's important rail, river ferry and port activities were badly affected. Erosion and changes to the river's course in places, significantly altered the sizes of some riverbank properties. The water also took days to drain away.

Possibly the most significant damage in the Norsewood area was to the nearly completed Kopua-Makotuku section of railway line. The tremendous slips on the new earthworks prevented it from opening for four months.

The flood in March had resulted in continuous work until Christmas. Flood in March? People tended to forget. It would soon be known as the Great Flood of 1880, with the details lost over time. Christian and his Norsewood gang had been at Tahoraiti, just beyond Dannevirke, when they were told there was no more work for them. They had been on the point of leaving for home when the weather broke.

Heavy rain fell continuously for days, and when it finally stopped for a few hours, Christian could bear it no longer. He had spent the days in the worker's quarters pacing back and forth like a caged tiger, consumed with fear for his family. When the rain suddenly stopped, he had headed home alone. His heart was in his mouth as he negotiated the Otamaraho Stream. He knew he should never have attempted such a foolhardy crossing. The land on the right side of him had been one huge lake. The road they had repaired, only the previous week, was now a sea of yellow mud that tried to suck him down or wash him away altogether. He was exhausted before he reached the Tamaki Stream, and there he stood horror-struck. The Tamaki

Bridge was askew and looked very dangerous. The grey, swirling torrent snatched at his feet. Bushes and even tall trees raced past him, beating against the quivering bridge as they fought their way to the sea.

Christian had no recollection of how he got back to Tahoraiti. Had an angel helped him over the first stream? All he remembered was seeing the door through the rain that was pouring down once more. He had been overcome by the strain of it all and had vomited. Then, after thanking God for his deliverance, he had pushed open the door and met the sea of grey faces staring back at him. He was cold and wet to the core.

After ten days the rain stopped. Then on the eleventh day, the sun shone from a cloudless sky – and the men left together for home. They needed each other's help to negotiate the swollen streams, however, the water levels had fallen quickly. A log-jam on the Mangatera had created a ford. Then in the late afternoon of 29 March, they reached their last hurdle – the Manga-te-wai-iti, 8 kilometres south of Norsewood. They had feared this deep valley, but instead they met a gang of workmates from home who were already busy repairing the bridge.

Yes, there had been heavy rain in Norsewood, and many slips around the district. Some were very bad. The district had been cut off from the outside world by floods elsewhere, but there had been no serious flooding close to the town.

Yes, children were back at school. No! No significant loss of stock around Norsewood that they knew of – and this was their third day working on the bridge.

The news calmed Christian considerably. He had spent days imagining flood water from the Manga-te-wai-nui swirling around their cottage, while Johanna and the three children clung to the roof. This was despite reassuring words to the contrary and knowing that Norsewood was rather higher than the surrounding district.

❁

The main road near Friberg Road, under the bright midday sun, was smooth and warm today. Christian and his gang had every reason to be proud of their work, which now stretched as far south as Ngawapurua, beyond Woodville, and to Te Apiti, at the very mouth of the Manawatu Gorge. Well, yes, proud in a sense, but in his heart of hearts he was sick of it. If the Makotuku contract eventuated, then . . .

Smoke was coming from the Olsens' chimney as he passed by. Anders must be safely home with his flour, and his Christine is baking. There will be a proper Christmas in that household too. A figure came out the door and walked quickly towards him. No, not Anders with his bandaged foot. It was Ole Blacksmith with his flax *kit*, which was now empty.

10 The curse of the Seventy-Mile-Bush

C AN there be many other cemeteries in New Zealand as beautifully situated, as lovingly tended – or as unique – as the one at Norsewood?

To walk amongst the headstones gives a very special feeling. Most of the old ones bear Norwegian names. The very air seems heavy with history. The first burial, a child from the first *Høvding* voyage, occurred shortly after the women and children arrived in Norsewood to join their menfolk in early October 1872. Bror Eric Friberg read the burial service over the grave. Perhaps this was Hilda Mathilde Pettersen, aged 19 months? Her headstone says she died on 20 October 1872.

As you enter the gate, a large uninterrupted patch of green is to your right (before you reach the big headstone of Bror Erik and Cecilia Friberg). No one knows with certainty who lies in this green area. The wooden crosses that once marked graves there were burnt in the big fire of 1888, and any new ones that may have replaced them have long since rotted away. However, we do know this was where children were buried after a tragic epidemic. I have found some of those names, but only some. Unfortunately, fire also consumed the church records.

As usual, it was Val Burr who found the essential documents dealing with the 1882 epidemic. It affected most of Hawke's Bay, however, the Seventy-Mile-Bush was hit particularly badly. Schoolchildren were the main victims and it was suspected that the illness was spread in the classroom.

We found only one list of names, with dates of birth and death – which contained a name of special interest to me . . .

Johanna felt depressed. There had been so many tragedies in the Seventy-Mile-Bush lately, and Norsewood families had suffered worst of all. While 1880 may have been the year of the flood and mass unemployment, 1882 was the year of death. More children died that year than in the previous five put together. No doctor could halt the epidemic that seemingly targeted school children. Rangna turned 6 that year and had started school at the end of February. They had been so proud of her, and so pleased when they accompanied her to school that summer morning.

Looking back, the new decade had started reasonably well for the family, all things considered, and was pregnant with promise. The first business trip to Dannevirke had been followed by others, and seemed to have been the beginning of something good and lasting. Johanna thought they were on a wave of good luck – at last! God be praised for that. She recalled Christmas 1880 with joy in her heart. Never before had there been so much good food on the table. And Martin Luther on the wall! He lifted her spiritually – such a good omen too. I may look strict, the green picture seemed to say, but if you follow my path, I shall look after you in this life – and beyond.

Both Johanna and Rangna had stopped coughing after the New Year, when the settled, warm weather came. Fear of the dreaded consumption waned month by month. The little girl picked up well, and although never of robust health, she appeared almost as strong as the other girls when starting school in early 1882. Thank God for that.

The New Year, following that memorable Christmas, had begun well for Christian too. Admittedly, he was out of work for some weeks, but Mrs Friberg had promised him a contract at her mill at Makotuku, as soon as it was ready to start. However, he did not return to roadwork. Thank God for that too. Instead, he found intermittent work at Mr Gundrie's small sawmill, the 'Railway Sawmill', near the railway station at Ormondville. A few months later, Mr Gundrie moved the mill to Garfield. In fact, to the sideroad adjoining Johanna and Christian's farm. It became known as Gundrie's Road.

It had been a wonderful autumn for clearing bush, and Christian had two successful burns that year – one before and one after Easter. The latter went on smoldering until extinguished by the winter rain in June. Mr Gundrie could be short of money and did not always pay his workers in cash. Instead, Christian often brought home building materials, so he could extend the cottage. To really extend it! From a hut to a house? Soon – perhaps. It was too good to believe. Still, over the months, lengths of timber came home on his shoulder at the end of each day's work.

Johanna was proud of him. Hard-working and dependable! Not once did he complain. His smile only became broader as the stocks of building material grew behind the cottage. One stack contained the heavy planking to be placed vertically on the outside. The other stack contained the fine thin boards that would one day be the inside lining. Only once did he borrow a horse and cart. That was the day the '4 by 2s' came home. No, not heart timber, Mr Gundrie could always sell that. A verandah was added to the cottage that winter, and best of all, another bedroom.

The future looked even brighter in November, when Christian became a contractor at Mrs Friberg's mill down Friberg Road, on the outskirts of Makotuku. Joseph was born that spring. They were a family of six now, and with so many mouths to feed, it was good to know money would be coming in regularly. Johanna felt secure at last.

Christian gave himself a holiday the day Rangna started school. He, too, wanted to accompany his little girl that morning – and he could afford the luxury. His tree-felling gang could manage very well without him. Lars, the oldest of the Larsen brothers, was in charge. Arne Shoemaker, sixteen years his senior, had found this a bitter pill to swallow. Still, there was no doubt about who was the champion bushman in Christian's section of Mrs Friberg's forest. Lars Larsen was the prizefighter of the giant trees. Arne had given him only a slight smile when they parted.

'Best of luck with your girl tomorrow.'

'Thanks. Many thanks.'

They regretted a little that Mr Thompson was not to be Rangna's teacher. He had opened the school in July 1873, but had resigned his position after a clash with the school inspector, William Colenso. He had been away for four years. Colenso had several bones to pick with Thompson. It annoyed him immensely that the teacher closed the school and sent the children home whenever there was a funeral.

Even more annoying was the general slackness regarding attendance. Half the school children could be away at any time, summer or winter. Slackness indeed! And the teacher used a fallacious argument as well – that the children had to help at home while their fathers were away working.

Colenso was highly indignant. This was child labour, akin to the mills of England. Thompson was obviously ignoring the regulations. He allowed truancy to take place under his very nose. One could say he encouraged it. The man was devious, hardly fit to be a teacher. That was not all. Thompson understood Norwegian. He was even known to have spoken it.

So Colenso made himself very clear. Only one language was to be used. English. English only! The children's futures were at stake! They were not to be used as cheap labour either . . . Oh, he knew these children well. Quiet as mice in the classroom. Too shy to get a sound out of them. But the moment they reached the playground, they would explode into incomprehensible babble. A handicap for life . . .

Colenso could, with some pleasure, report to the Hawke's Bay Education Board in 1877, that Mr Thompson had resigned and Miss E. Ross would take over. The new teacher was very well qualified. She even spoke French and German as well as she spoke English. By the time Rangna started, though, Miss Ross (by then Mrs E. Thomson) was already gone.* Mr Bruford was now holding the educational fort, and there was no doubt that school attendance had improved. Equally good, the school no longer closed as a general practice for funerals. Still, what was the language spoken in the playground? Was it still that barbaric babble? Colenso wanted to discover this for himself. Outside he met bow-legged little Julius, Randi's precious son.

'Yes sir, I like going to school.'

'Yes sir, Mr Bruford is a good teacher.'

'Yes sir, we all speak English now.'

The boy spoke very good English! Colenso felt relieved. Stricter discipline was paying off, that was obvious.

The settlers recalled Mr Thompson† as a man to be relied upon. He knew the settlers, their needs and their children. He knew schooling required more than just the 3Rs. As a sign of respect, fathers traditionally escorted their children to school on their first day. Mr Thompson would welcome them and there would be handshaking and enquiries made about the health of the family. How many smaller children were still at home, and how was the father's work? Nothing hurried. Nothing officious. Mr Thompson could be trusted

---

* Although unconfirmed, she is possibly the Mrs Thompson [sic] of Norsewood, who had opened the first Makotuku School, as a branch of Norsewood School, in spring 1878. This first school was conducted in the Friberg house, Garfield [formerly Friberg] Road.

† Mr Thompson left Norsewood at the end on 1885 to become headmaster of Matamau School, which is between Norsewood and Dannevirke. His wife Brunhilde also opened a shop in Matamau.

to do the right thing, and when to do it. When to close the school. And when to take the service himself at the graveside because Reverend Edward Nielsen needed assistance. Reverend Nielsen travelled such a lot to preach the Gospel. He had a very large parish and a very scattered flock. In his absence, only Mr Thompson had been there to take his place. However, before he could say the comforting words over the coffin, the school first had to be closed – so close the school he did. However, his return in May 1882 from Kile School, Ashburton, upon the recommendation of the school committee, was not marked by happy celebration.

The *Hawke's Bay Herald*'s Ormondville correspondent had announced, on 20 April 1882, the planned departure for Auckland of the well-liked Mr Bruford. It also informed readers that almost every family in the Norsewood, Ormondville, Makotuku district included a sufferer of bronchitis and measles: 'in some cases in an aggravated form. Considering the scattered population of the Bush districts, there has been quite as much death here as in Napier.' As well as speculating on the cause of the dilemma, the report added Ormondville School was soon to reopen: 'but it is a question whether many of the children will be in a fit state to attend.'

Norsewood's correspondent to the same newspaper had graphically described the town's dilemma as at 4 April. The local cemetery committee had applied to enlarge the cemetery due to the recent pressure, from a wide area, upon its services:

> *I regret to say that the space hitherto set apart for the burial of the dead has been filling up altogether too rapidly lately, and I fear that more room will be required, unless the measles, scarlatina, and diphtheria, so prevalent in our district, are speedily stamped out. Over thirty children are laid up at present, and our school is of course still closed.*

Anna Maria Christina Larsen and Anna Olsen, both aged 7 years, had died four weeks earlier. From that time, half the children stayed away from school. No one knew how or where the epidemic really started, and no doctor produced any satisfactory diagnosis or remedy. Poor Mr Bruford had been at his wits' end, especially when rumours spread that the school's drinking water was contaminated. After the third child died, he locked the schoolroom, closed the gate and emptied the water tank. An article in the *Hawke's Bay Herald* of 17 May, added that:

> At the meeting of the (Hawke's Bay) Education Board yesterday Mr Hill stated that he had the authority of the Registrar of Deaths for saying that in five weeks recently more deaths occurred in Norsewood than in five years previously, the whole of the mortality being among children. Mr Hill thought the sickness commenced with measles, but before the sufferers fully recovered they were allowed to run about in the open air, barefooted and bareheaded, with the result that diphtheria was brought on. The Board decided to adopt a suggestion thrown out in our columns a short time ago, and to have the water from the wells in the neighbourhood analysed by Doctor Hector.

Who was this Dr Hector? Did anyone ever see him in Norsewood? Johanna was scared. Very scared. When Mr Thompson arrived in late May and had suggested ways to care for the children, Johanna had followed his advice to the letter. Keep the children at home, boil all drinking water, and avoid contact with other families.

Sound advice, and most mothers did their very best. But it was a struggle to keep restless and adventurous boys at home – away from their friends. Five boys had died during the first half of April, only one below school age. Six girls, all school age, passed away later that month. Another six died in early May. Johanna knew all the parents. Why did God punish them all? Martin Luther, on the wall, could not provide an answer.

If only they had a doctor! But with the closest at Woodville and Waipukurau, it fell upon Mr Thompson to do his best.

He visited the grieving families, but his offers of condolence and words of comfort, both in the homes and at gravesides, were largely lost on the shattered families. They needed answers from God. Had they really been so wicked? Was this just punishment meted out to them? Where had they gone so wrong?

With regard to worldly matters, Mr Thompson had the same advice as before . . . 'Boil all drinking water, and keep the children at home.'

Mr Thompson was requested by the Education Board to reopen the school by 1 June. Supposedly the epidemic had run its course.

Still, Johanna knew of several children who were still sick. Had the danger really passed? Would it be safe to send little Rangna back to school?

She remained on the road watching her daughter long after she had released her warm little hand. A quick hug and – be a good girl – then Rangna had walked off joyfully. Her plaits danced around her ears, the precious school slate pressed against her body, and her lunch, wrapped in fabric from a flour bag, in her pocket. A picture of happy anticipation. She stopped several times and waved to her mother, before disappearing around the bend in the road. Oh, my dear little girl. My precious, precious little girl.

The school remained open until mid-July. However, when death claimed several more children within a week, Mr Thompson locked the school door once more. It was not as if there were many pupils attending regularly by then anyway, as Mr Thompson habitually sent children home as soon as they started coughing.

Was Rangna a little pale? Did she seem listless? She didn't toss her plaits as before, or use her school slates for new words or animal pictures. She wasn't interested, not in helping with milking either, even though they had a new calf. Johanna watched her silently, anxiety rising increasingly, like a small creek becoming a stream and then a river – then flooding her mind. Please God; tell me I'm wrong! That I'm just seeing things!

During August, Rangna began coughing and seemed weak. Johanna made up a new bed for her in the room Christian had built, and put her to bed. The smaller children were not to enter, to reduce the risk of them also becoming infected. Horror filled her when she thought of the family at Te Whiti on the German Line. There everyone, large and small, had been infected. The three daughters had been buried just outside the house, as the father lacked the strength to take them to the cemetery.

No help had been available as their home was quite remote from those of their neighbours. When people eventually noticed their non-appearance and called on them, it had been too late. Had those little bodies ever made it to sanctified soil? Johanna did not know. It sounded like the Great Plague all over again – that terrible story she had once learned in Odalen from the itinerant teacher.

September came with an early spring and sunny weather, but Rangna grew weaker. She would not recover. They knew it was only a question of time before they would lose her. Christian had tried to cure her with spoonfuls of port wine – as with Julius aboard *Høvding* – but nothing worked.

Johanna sat with her most of the time. She held her warm little hand, and dabbed cold water from a basin onto her hot forehead when the fever raged. She told Rangna of the blueberries in the Skara forest, and calmed the other children when they made too much noise.

Very little was done in the garden or in the house. Christine Olsen, her neighbour, came over with dinner on two occasions. A traditional Eastern Norway stew with plenty of potatoes – just heavenly. But, oh God! How could she afford it? The Olsens were so hard up.

The afternoon of 15 September saw Christian, as usual, in the Makotuku bush. Work was going well. They had an easy section to fell that was close to the mill. The tramline for extracting the heavy logs with bullock teams worked well in this part of the bush, while the screeching of saws, like ever-hungry demons demanding more and more sacrifices, could be heard above everything else.

Johanna had been at Rangna's side all day. The fever had increased that morning, just after Christian left for work. This time, cold wet flannels did not seem to work. At least not for long. Tales of the blueberry forest had lost their magic and Rangna had entered her own world of fantasies. The hot, flustered child lay in her bed, her eyes wide open, with her mother holding her hand. Hours passed. It seemed perhaps she was regaining her strength when she squeezed her mother's hand.

'Mama?'

'Yes, my darling?'

'I love you so.' Then the small hand's strength left it entirely.

Two very serious little boys met Christian at dusk as he returned from work. He knew from their faces what had happened, well before they burst into tears and tried to explain. He found Johanna where he had left her that morning, but now bent over the bed, her shoulders shaking. They clung to each other tightly and wept together as dusk turned to darkness.

Later, by candlelight, they knelt by the bed, prayed and sang the few hymns they still remembered from their confirmation lessons. Carl August and little Johan remained with them, and were of considerable comfort to their parents.

The burial took place the next day. Randi, with Julius, joined them at the graveside, as did Fredrik. Everyone else had enough of their own problems to deal with – and there had been so many similar funerals. Thank God, Reverend Nielsen was in Norsewood that week. His words about Jesus going ahead to prepare a room in the Heavenly Mansion for Rangna soothed Johanna. Reverend Nielsen was so kind

– and he spoke the proper language. Every word was understood.

There were twenty small white crosses in the cemetery that day – 16 September 1882. Further heaps of fresh soil showed where other children – with crosses still to come – had also been interred.

My friend Vince Mortensen, 80 years of age, was proud of two things. He was the only one left in Norsewood who was of pure Norwegian descent, and he lived in Norsewood's oldest cottage. The kitchen and fireplace of this well-maintained house have remained unchanged since it was built in 1873.

Vince was a mine of information and my very special guide at Norsewood between January and March 1997. He showed me where Drower's store had been, Olsen's smithy, the Lutheran church, the Methodist church, and all the important landmarks of the 1880s. We met at the Crown Hotel every Thursday evening, and his tales and anecdotes were endless.

Vince was not able to document anything, so for hard historical facts I had to return to Val Burr with her gift for research.

Above all, Vince was a storyteller. He was in no doubt that the 1880s were the hardest and bleakest years in Norsewood's history. Financially, they were getting on their feet, the land was slowly being cleared and farming was beginning to take off. But they were beset with accidents, unemployment, deaths and mishaps. Had the devil himself put a curse on the district?

While I was writing this book back in Norway, I learned that Vince Mortensen had died. His great wish to go 'home' to Odalen was, therefore, never fulfilled. *Takk for Alt.*

'My Father's house has many rooms . . .' The sacred text lived with Johanna for a very long time. She had heard those words before, even learnt the four verses off by heart at her confirmation classes, but now they had taken on a new meaning. Jesus had gone ahead and prepared a room for Rangna. Rangna had her own room in Heaven. Own room!

It was hard to fathom. God's generosity and kindness was beyond human understanding. Still, a room implied walls. They would not be of rimu. Surely not. Something light and airy, perhaps. Something transparent, so you could see into the next room. Maybe into many rooms. She would not like Rangna to feel lonely in Heaven. There would be other little girls living in the other rooms. Floor? Not of matai. Too hard and noisy. No floor at all, most likely. Souls were light. They could fly and needed no structure. Were they angels then? Had Rangna become an angel and retained her human form?

There was nobody Johanna could discuss these questions with. Christian could only hold her hand when she thought aloud, or stroke her hair calmingly. And, Johanna did not know then that her grandmother, Maren, wife of Old Paso, was a new arrival to her own Heavenly room at that time. That knowledge would have comforted her.

There had been times when she had remonstrated with God – and with Martin Luther. Why was she punished? Where had they deviated from His path? Self-recrimination soon followed. Why did I send my child to school that day? Why did I obey the school authorities? If only . . . If only . . . She pushed these thoughts aside. Negative, harmful questions, whether spiritual or of this world. And there would never be an answer anyway.

Please God, let me hold onto what is good. Let me just see Rangna as she was that morning, with her warm little hand in mine, plaits bobbing around her ears, one arm holding onto the slate that gave her so much pleasure. Turning, nodding and smiling, waving with her free hand – before being swallowed up by the trees. Thank God for that picture. Let it stay in my mind. In my treasure chest – to be brought out in dark moments.

And dark moments there were. The following year, big brother Fredrik passed away. Unhappy Fredrik. Nothing seemed to have gone right for him – and then consumption claimed him as well. His marriage had not been a success.

– 184 –

Nasty woman too – please forgive me God! It was a joyless union. Trapped into marriage, yet she gave him no child. A wicked mystery, and now his sad, short life was already over, just one day before his thirtieth birthday.

The epidemic passed, but the religious revival sweeping through the Seventy-Mile-Bush was at a high point. Never had there been so many prayer meetings in homes. Never had so many turned to Him for guidance and help and never had His house been sought by so many. All turned up for church on Sundays. Only by receiving His support on His day, could they face the week ahead. The Lutheran church was built in Lower Norsewood the year Rangna died. It became Johanna's second home. Her spirit was renewed there, her courage regained.

Johanna had almost forgotten that God had shown great mercy to her two years earlier. It had all been so close. So close she shuddered at the thought of what could have happened. The well had a new heavy lid after that episode.

Carl August, the fearless little adventurer, was only 3 then. He had often been with Johanna to fetch water from the well Arne Shoemaker and Christian had dug. No one saw him toddle off that afternoon, carrying a bucket almost as big as he was. But Johanna heard the splash and the piercing screams. Her blood froze. Thank God the rope was in place, on the nail on the wall. And thank God again, that Carl wore the standard dress of all toddlers and small children – a wide skirt. God be praised – it must have trapped the air and kept him afloat – despite his flailing arms. Johanna could see him quite clearly. His light blue dress contrasted against the black water.

'Hold onto the rope, Carl.' She tried to sound calm. Twice she had him almost to the edge of the well. Twice he fell back with heart-rending screams. Please God, Please. Dick, the 13-year-old motherless boy who had more or less attached himself to Johanna's household, came to the rescue.

'Will you? Can you? Oh, you must . . .' It all happened in

a flash. Over the edge, hand over hand down the well, his feet touching the sides. He grabbed the sky blue bundle, now low in the water, tied the rope under the child's flailing arms, while maintaining his own precarious position by pressing his back and his feet against the well's sides.

'Quick! Haul!' And Dick was left behind in the wet darkness. The screaming blue bundle was untied, shooed home unceremoniously, and the rope thrown back into the well. Despite cold fingers already turning blue and stiff, Dick managed to tie the rope around his waist. Johanna anchored herself behind a stump and together, one hauling, one climbing, the young hero returned to the surface. Hero indeed! Johanna was loud in his praises. So loud and so persistent in fact, she almost forgot to praise Him, the true deliverer.

Johanna suffered moments of depression for a long time after this incident, and these occurred more often as the epidemic raged through the Seventy-Mile-Bush. God was not on their side. She was in danger of losing her way. Martin Luther on the wall looked particularly stern and a little worried.

Yet, after Fredrik's death, Johanna knew for sure she was back with God. That Sunday morning in the new Lutheran Church, still smelling of fresh wood, she experienced something unusual. She had found herself reliving the storm they had encountered aboard *Høvding* ten years earlier in the South Atlantic.

Was it late September? Was it early October? Was it exactly ten years ago? Memories flooded her mind. She saw the ship plunge down, down, into the deep dark valleys, felt it shudder and shake before straightening and climbing out of the abyss. She saw the three masts swinging in great arcs against the grey wind-torn sky. Clouds raced past while the wind howled through the rigging. The sails were furled, but the swinging spars groaned under the strain. Only the mizzen staysail, with its canvas half shortened, still remained in place.

Part pictures flashed before her inner eye. She saw herself drenched, the salt water stinging her eyes. And the helmsman? No, it was not second mate Olassen or the tussle-haired able seaman, or the ship's carpenter with eyes as blue as the smiling Atlantic . . . No, not any of them. It was Johanna herself. It was she who was lashed to the wheel to ensure she would not be washed overboard. It was she who was fighting to keep the ship on course. And it was she who was responsible for everyone's lives.

Still, in her inner world, Johanna had felt there had been another helmsman at her side, and it was His advice she had followed.

'Be strong. Hold on. Keep the same course. The storm will pass and you will be a better helmsman after this test.'

The reliving had seemed so real. Johanna felt she really had been through a storm and now, thank God, she was back on an even keel. No! More than that. Now she was stronger. She felt she had gained the advice of the Great Helmsman himself.

Hold on. Be strong. And it was such personal advice. As far as she was concerned, it was a real message to her from God.

There were other ships in the Norsewood district at that time that were tossed dangerously on high and perhaps without a helmsman at all. Emily and her Danish family at Makaretu were caught in a storm that broke their ship. Mama Randi knew Emily from her year as the wife of Hans Andersen, the Makaretu storekeeper.

'Such a lovely person, so sweet and sensitive. Artistic too. But I don't think she was suited to the hard life in the bush.'

Emily had drifted into depression after her young daughter died, but perhaps no one knew the extent of her condition. Knowing Emily's husband and only son were away bush-clearing, her neighbour had called one morning in mid-May, to cheer her up. The door was locked, and the blinds were down. Fearing the worst, she peeped through an uncovered section of window. She froze when she saw an upturned chair on the floor, and . . .

Mama Randi was deeply upset by the suicide. 'It was too much for poor Emily. She could not get over the loss of her daughter.'

The storm that broke over Elise the following month was vicious, but it did not sink her ship. Johanna knew her well. She lived quite close and had been a member of the 'Wednesday Club.' They also shared the same surname – Christiansen. Her husband had been killed two years earlier in a tree-felling accident and now her house had burnt down. Elise and her four young children had found themselves homeless and destitute. Still, she was courageous, hard-working, and liked and respected by everyone. She insisted she could manage on her own, but how could she with no house and no income?

Johanna wanted to foster two of the children, but Christian was adamant. He would have nothing to do with it. After all, little Rolf had been born only a few months after Rangna's death.

'You have four boys to look after, more than enough to keep your hands full. I can help Elise with a little money, and there are others who will do that too. I've already talked it over with Constable Shultz and we'll place a subscription list for Elise in Drower's store.'

It was not like Christian to be so determined concerning family matters, but he worried about Johanna's health. And then there was Dick, who stayed with them with increasing frequency.

'If I know Elise right, she'll get over it. She is very strong – and she is too proud anyway to let anyone foster her children.'

There the matter ended. However, while Johanna might not have been permitted to look after other people's children, Christian ensured she was abundantly blessed with her own. The year following Rolf's birth, Johanna recognised the familiar symptoms of pregnancy again. Would it be a girl this time? Please God? She wished and sincerely hoped it would be a new Rangna. Each day she asked God for that in her prayers.

God heard her prayers. The little girl was born on a summer's day in 1884. She was christened Rangna.

The economic cloud hanging over Norsewood may have started dispersing as the mid-1880s drew to a close, but the district curse was not lifted. The Ormondville tragedy, Johanna thought, was the worst by far. Here there was no talk of a storm or a ship or a helmsman. No, this was a cyclone. A whirlwind perhaps, let loose by the devil himself. The central person in this tragedy was Roland Herbert Edwards – not a Scandinavian, thank God. Still, he had lived and worked among them. And in a moment of madness he had killed his entire family.

The *Hawke's Bay Herald* of 12 February had begun its months of coverage with:

> *Tragedy at Ormondville: A shocking murder has been committed here, and our usually quiet township has been consequently thrown into a state of feverish excitement, tempered with profound gloom, such as no pen can adequately describe. The scene of this terrible crime is a small cottage, containing two rooms, situated about 100 yards to the left of the railway line between Ormondville and Makotuku. Externally, the cottage and its surroundings look calm and peaceful, the well-tended garden affording evidence that the inmates of the cottage were possessed of taste and energy. In the small dwelling resided a man named Roland Edwards, his wife and four children, whose ages ranged from a few months to ten years . . .*

Alcohol was behind it all. Johanna was adamant about that. His poor wife had tried to curb his drinking bouts – but did anyone help her? Or him for that matter? Not the barman anyway! She had pleaded with him, the one at Ormondville's hotel, the Settler's Arms, not to sell that Satan's brew to her husband. Did he take any notice? Oh no, not him. As long as there was money left in Mr Edwards' pocket, the barman would continue to fill his glass. Shocking! Johanna was indignant beyond words. She had seen men fighting outside the Junction Hotel, in Lower Norsewood, on Saturday nights. Money that was meant to feed children was wasted on beer. Meanwhile grown men turned into snarling animals. Johanna was strong in her views regarding alcohol.

'Mr Edwards became violent when drunk. In fact he was simply dangerous. Everyone knew that. The doctors and police knew it, and what was more, they knew he was mentally ill as well.'

'Poor sick man. An asylum was the place for him. Should have been there long ago. They knew he was a violent drunkard as well. He had often beaten his wife black and blue, and had even tried to blow her up with gunpowder. She went to the hotel – and that would take some courage, don't you think? She begged and pleaded that her husband should be served no more. Courageous woman she was. Fighting for her family, but where did it get her? Where did it get her that Sunday night of 10–11 February 1884?'

People gathered in groups when the newspapers reached Drower's store that summer, autumn and early winter of 1884. Articles and the court case involving Roland Herbert Edwards were read aloud and commentaries were louder still. The whole district took part in this case. Everyone was a jury member. Proper justice was to be done.

The 'inadequate pens' in the various newspapers had no difficulty describing the scene in depth. Further embellishment, with elegant turn of phrase and gruesome detail, followed over subsequent weeks. The reading public learned, repeatedly, how poor Mary Edwards and four of her five children died. Her oldest child had been staying elsewhere that night for its own safety.

People were furious. Action was needed. Not just endless discussion and argument. Not just words, words, words . . . Who started the anti-alcohol campaign that was to spread through the district like wildfire? No one really knew. Indeed, it was like a scrub fire on a hot summer's day. Ignited somewhere, somehow, in many places at the same time. It engulfed the whole region and indeed the country. Johanna found herself engulfed as well. She had been one of the four or five hundred mourners who followed the sad little procession to the tiny bush clearing that had only recently been declared Ormondville's cemetery.

For weeks, despite being tied to her babies, her kitchen stove and her farm duties, she assisted with the petition circulating throughout the district. However, she worked even harder to encourage support for those men standing on the 'Temperance ticket,' in the forthcoming election for the Norsewood Licensing Committee. Many more people now felt strongly that there was no need for licensed hotels in the district – especially at Ormondville!

For Johanna, calling on neighbours and friends was a pleasant task. It was not difficult to persuade them to sign either, as they all knew the evil associated with strong drink. Her 'English Class' had been in recess since the epidemic of 1882 (and was fated never to resume), but her former 'pupils' signed willingly. And better still, most of their menfolk also signed. Could the men really be trusted though? Men fell so easily by the wayside when it came to Saturday nights with their mates, but they meant well, at least for the moment.

Hundreds of signatures and promises regarding the election came in from Norsewood, Makaretu, Ormondville, Makotuku, Matamau and parts between. This was serious business. The petition would soon be on its way to Parliament requesting that hotel liquor licenses be withdrawn. And, of course, and perhaps more importantly, the Licensing Committee election was imminent . . .

Mr Linehan, the publican at the Settlers Arms, felt the intense pressure and was soon fighting his attackers through the pages of the *Hawke's Bay Herald*. The Temperance men predominated on the new Norsewood Licensing Committee and in June they cancelled the liquor licenses held by the hotels at Norsewood, Ormondville, Makotuku and Matamau. Their district, at least, was now 'dry.' It would be three years before any licenses were returned. Even then, it took a lot of law-stretching, some sly grog selling and the declaration of a tiny new, more liberal licensing district covering only the railway towns of Ormondville and Makotuku. Norsewood, however, remained dry. Still, all this did not affect Publican Linehan. He had sold up and, with his new wife and their newborn baby, he had left the district within weeks of the murders.

The district had been in the grips of religious fervour for much of the early 1880s. Was this just another face of the revival movement?

No, it was not God inspired. True, many tried to speak for Him. The old biblical arguments, about an eye for an eye, were heard more than once. God was strict. God punishes. Did he not smite the Israelites as well as the Philistines? He smote them hard too. The lot of them.

No. Not again. This fervour was not of a spiritual nature. The petition that went to Parliament was about common decency. About family life. It was about justice.

Johanna was in no doubt as to the part played by the publican. He was guilty of a crime in the eyes of the Lord, surely. God would punish him eventually. Justice would be meted out to him, either in this life or in the hereafter. God was just. He would not forget. She felt confident about His part.

Still, was there another side to this tragedy that the reporters had so many big words for? Why did everyone focus on the publican? The doctors and the police knew Edwards was mad. They had sent him to an asylum for assessment after earlier irrational incidents. But once there he had appeared sane, had been declared sane, and had therefore been sent home. Perhaps they were all guilty? The police and the doctors. The judge wanted to hang Edwards. Would he let the others off? Was it left to God alone to show justice? Was human law like that? To protect the ones in power and punish the weak ones? Johanna was deeply troubled, but she would pursue her anti-alcohol campaign until her dying day. Luckily Christian also knew that Satan lurked in bottles and bars. Eventually, Edwards was hanged.

Her faith in God was not shaken by the Ormondville tragedy. Far from it. Even when she had come close to losing Christian, she had remained strong. Seemingly calm outwardly and strong inwardly. She now felt she could cope with whatever fate or life put in front of her. She would remain the helmsman of her family and steer the course that God had set for her. But Johanna would be tested sorely.

Pig hunting was such a stupid idea anyway. She would never eat pork herself. Not from any source, neither the bush nor the butcher. Nor would she even cook it in her home. It was that Arne Shoemaker who, once more, had organised this! Instead of coming home on a Friday evening after work, they were to head directly for the Ngamoko bush.

'It is just on the edge of the bush anyway,' Arne had said. 'Do a little pig hunting before it gets dark. The place is lousy with pigs. Just the three of us, you and me, and Caesar. Might do a little at dawn on Saturday. Borrowed Jens' horse to bring it all back. Could be home Friday night. You can never tell.'

It all sounded very simple. Johanna lacked Arne's enthusiasm for Caesar, and he was clearly to be the main hunter. Caesar was now well past his youth. His arthritic legs and grey muzzle indicated he was set on the downward slope of old age. Obvious to everyone except Arne, that is.

'He is better than ever. Hear that growl! See those eyes – yellow with ferocity! Hackles rising, see! No wonder all the pigs between Ngamoko and Manawatu fear him.'

True, Caesar's temper had not become milder with age.

Johanna had not expected her husband to come home that Friday night. The pigs may not be as plentiful as promised, and old Caesar could be past holding pigs or bailing them up.

Then Saturday came and went. Johanna felt uneasy towards dusk, and the boys had started asking questions.

'Papa will be home soon. Soon! Just after you go to bed.'

Arne, Caesar and the horse came back after church on Sunday. There was no sign of Christian though. They had become separated on Saturday morning. Arne was a little vague on details. But it transpired that Caesar had picked up the scent at dawn – clever dog that! However, he had lost it high in the hills sometime later. Unbelievable! There had been so many pigs. All extremely fast and cunning. Still, of course they knew the terrain, and had that advantage over Caesar.

The men had followed, but then . . . Oh! Arne had sprained his ankle, see, it's all black and blue – and had limped back to camp. Caesar had joined him that evening, a footsore and very hungry old dog. Caesar's day had been exhausting. No wonder he slept so well and no longer felt like chasing pigs this morning. And that was the extent of Arne's report. However, he was going back to Ngamoko that evening on horseback to see if Christian had turned up.

Monday came and went . . .

Local people formed search parties, including Christian's workmates from the latest sawmill to which his team was contracted. Workmates from previous mills also assisted. (Mrs Friberg had, unfortunately, gone bankrupt in 1883 and her mill had been sold.) Shots were fired in the air, but to no avail. Johanna felt strangely calm. She knew God would keep His part of their understanding. Since the 'vision' in the

Lutheran church, she felt she had entered a covenant with Him. She would be the helmsman of the family ship. She would remain strong, and would steer a steady course. And He would keep His protective hand over them all.

Tuesday – and Christian arrived home at dusk. He was tired and dirty, but in good spirits. The whole family knelt by the big table and thanked the Lord for his safe delivery.

Christian had been so very, very lucky. He had left Ashhurst at dawn that morning, prepared to walk all the way home to Norsewood. Instead, he had received no less than six lifts. The first took him through the Manawatu Gorge to Woodville. The last, a carter on his way home to Waipawa, included sharing the carter's food.

Christian had little to say about his ordeal in the bush. No, he had not been very scared. He felt that God had held his hand over him. Yes, he had followed Caesar – he thought – for many hours. He had crossed a steep ridge and had avoided some nasty bluffs on his left, and by dark he had found himself in a deep valley. He had seen Tunupo Peak to the north early in the day, and Toka a little later.

Eventually he found himself in what he hoped was the Pohangina Valley, a destination then unfamiliar to non-Maori people. He slept under a rimu near the river he'd found and had eaten some of his smoked eel. Only some, though, as he knew he might still have long days ahead of him in the bush. He knew that by following the river – and how he prayed he was right – to its junction with the Manawatu River near Ashhurst, he would be safer than if he attempted to get back to Ngamoko.

There had been a difficult gorge to deal with the next morning, where the river turned west, but apart from that it had been easy walking. He mainly followed the riverbed – until he reached safety in the village of Ashhurst early on Monday evening. The weather was still warm that late summer, and the river remained low. God had indeed looked after him.

Arne Shoemaker presented him with a new pair of boots before church, that Palm Sunday.

Christian knew others had lost their lives in the bush, yet he made light of his adventure. Johanna, too, seemed oblivious of the dangers that could have befallen him. Other mental pictures seemed to be preying on her.

The well. Above all, it was the well. And not just the close encounter with little Carl August . . . Auntie Kari's letter from Odalen kept returning to her mind. Dear Auntie. She was not a very gifted letter writer and her spelling was poor, but the meaning was always clear. And her items of news were of the greatest importance. She and Uncle Arne, Johan's older brother, had decided against coming to Ny Seland. Instead, there had been two letters over six years.

The first letter had described a near tragedy. Old Paso had fallen into a well. Furthermore, it had happened in February, when it was bitterly cold and the land was deep in snow. Grandpa, with his long staff and his Bible, had set out one morning to walk from one farm to the next, as the parish's Council for the Poor had directed. More snow had fallen overnight and all the tracks were obliterated. And the lid had not been placed back on the well . . .

Old Paso was not missed. He was expected at the next farm, but the people there were not alarmed when he did not arrive. They simply assumed he had stayed at the previous farm until the weather cleared. Dear old Grandpa. He was in the well two whole days and nights. Praise the Lord, the ice was thick enough to hold him. On the third morning, a servant girl who had come to draw water was convinced she had seen a ghost in the well.

The doctor who examined Grandpa thought a near miracle had occurred. He was soon declared fit to travel on. Oh, Old Paso must have been strong, both in body and spirit. However, an argument developed between the doctor and the well's owner, over who would pay the doctor's fee.

Johanna shed many tears over this incident, both then and when in the future she was reminded of it.

The next letter from Auntie Kari brought more sad news. Old Paso had peacefully passed away one late autumn day in 1878. He was glad to know his family in Ny Seland was doing well and that Johan and Ole had started their own blacksmithing business. He was happy, Aunty Kari wrote, as he departed this world. Many more tears were shed when this news came.

Dear Old Paso – Grandpa. Always seeing the best in people. Always wise and cheerful, and always thinking of the next generation. Johanna had only told him the good things, and their plans for the future. She could not bring herself to tell him that Johan had died less than three years after reaching Ny Seland.

11 The great fire

O N 14 February 1888, the *Hawke's Bay Herald*'s Norsewood correspondent scribbled out his regular report. 'The remarkable continuance of uninterrupted dry weather that has been experienced in this and the surrounding settlements has perhaps been felt more severely than one generally supposes. For some considerable time we have had no rainfall beyond a few showers, the effects of which have disappeared the following day. The consequence is that although the weather has often been much cooler than the time of year would warrant, the continued drought in the absence of fog and dews has shrivelled up the grass, and cattle have had to be fed on dry dust and rotten bark.'

Perhaps the cattle feed was exaggerated, but conditions were certainly poor. Milk supplies were badly affected and the year's grass seed crop – the district's 'chief industry' at that time – was considered barely worth cutting. Furthermore, burn-off fires raged in all directions and some fences on the Danish Line (now Norsewood-Ormondville Road) had already been destroyed. Men were forced to be 'up day and night watching for the safety of the dwellings. Trees are thundering down around us without the inevitable thud of the axe, peculiar to bush-falling districts. I hear that one house has already succumbed to the devouring element.'

The following month began with little change – however, nationally March 1888 became noted for above average rainfall and high winds . . .

Was Old Paso with the angels? Had he been able to look down all these years, and see how they really lived? Johanna had told him of their big farm and their big plans for the future. Everything was cheerful and big in her letters. Big trees – and a big job to clear them. Big fires in the autumn every year, to create big paddocks for the big herds of cattle.

Was Grandpa annoyed with her for having been less than truthful? She had meant well – and no one could dispute the big trees and the big fires anyway. A pall of smoke hung over the Seventy-Mile-Bush, and well beyond, from February to April each year. You could smell fire for weeks on end, even if you could not see it. And the smoke could be so thick perhaps the angel Gabriel himself could not see what lay beneath the billowing grey blanket.

Was the acrid smell stronger than usual today though? Johanna thought, as she felt it burning her nostrils. Her eyes stung as well. The Ruahine Ranges were invisible, not sharp and clear against the deep blue sky as they usually were. The air was still. Still, heavy and warm. In fact, it was unusually warm for this time of morning – and unusually still after the northwest gale that had been blowing for days. A smoky haze filled the world to the north, and seemed to come from somewhere behind Norsewood. A slate-grey ocean, slightly blue at the top with a haze of red underneath, but without waves, wrinkles or movements. Johanna felt strangely on edge.

With the first puff of wind, the ocean began moving. A warm wind, again from the northwest, that increased rapidly in strength. And the smoke ocean was on the verge of engulfing them all. Eyes watered, and the smell of burnt wood tore at nostrils. Johanna understood the seriousness of it all. The fire was out of control. It was high time to act, but to do what exactly . . .

The children! Where were they? Should she bring them inside? No, they were not safe there. The bush was still quite close, not to mention the tree skeleton still standing nearby and the rotting logs lying about.

'Carl August!' She shouted louder than necessary. A new note had come into her voice as well. The boy had been kept home to help his mother that morning and was behind the house. He wondered if it was time now to go to school – and should he take his marbles and knucklebones?

'Yes, Mama?'

The smoke was heavier and the wind much stronger by the time Johanna had collected up the children. Carl August was instructed to take the other children to Auntie Berte's, in Lower Norsewood. There was not as much bush there. They would be safer.

'You had better piggyback little Fredrik. He's not very heavy. Tell Auntie Berte that I'll come as soon as I can.'

What should she herself do next though? Should she stay at the house or should she leave? No. Perhaps better to remain to see if she could protect the house.

Johanna walked part of the way with the children, then bade them a quick farewell. She watched as they disappeared around the next corner into the stinging smoke. Little Rangna, aged 4 and named after a sister who would have been 12 this year, led the way. Behind her were Johan, Josef and then Rolf. Last in line was Carl August, with Fredrik on his back. He turned at the corner and waved reassuringly back to his mother. A grey shadow in a grey world.

The house looked empty and forlorn. The hens had vanished and the cows no longer contentedly chewed their cud in their paddock. They and the sheep had drifted towards the apparent security of the stream.

Johanna was barely home before Christine, her neighbour, came running towards her. Christine was highly agitated, and had also sent her children to the presumed safety of Lower Norsewood.

'It's coming this way, Johanna! The fire is on its way!' She grabbed hold of Johanna's arm, squeezed it hard in her panic, and appeared reluctant to let it go.

'Oh my God! Where are they? Anders and Christian! Why are they not here?' She was almost hysterical.

Johanna wanted to pacify her. She wanted to show courage and comfort Christine with soothing words, but failed sadly. She was also scared, really scared! The wind's strength now resembled a hurricane and was coming in hot bursts from beyond the Ruahine Ranges. The thick smoke now contained particles of burning wood, which stung like angry bees.

'The men will soon be here if they think we're in real danger. You know that! Perhaps they think the fire is moving in another direction. Or perhaps they know it will burn itself out before reaching here.' Johanna managed to say these things calmly, despite struggling with her own fear and being quite unable to think. What should they do? Stay?

In a moment, the decision was taken from them. A horseman galloped from the smoke and sharply halted his sweating horse beside them. It was Lars Larsen, his hair singed like his horse's, and his face sooty. He and two other mill-workers had ridden through the fire, to warn of the impending danger.

No. He could not stay. There were others to be contacted. The fire would probably reach this spot within the hour and all Norsewood could burn!

'Get your things out of the house. Quickly! Save what you can. Leave them on the road. Someone will come for them. Hurry. Leave for Lower Norsewood very soon,' he said, placing special emphasis on the 'very.' With that, he dug his heels into the horse's heaving sides.

Johanna grabbed Lars' foot. The plunging horse pivoted around her.

'How is Christian? Where is he?'

'They are safe at the mill. Behind the fire! It's this way that the fire is travelling.' With that, man and horse were gone. Swallowed up by the smoke, leaving only the sound of the horse's galloping hooves on the gravel road.

Christine, white as a ghost moments earlier, now ran in the opposite direction. Suddenly, she knew what to do.

The wind was now a raging storm, a firestorm filled with burning projectiles. An army on the march, advancing with fixed bayonets and guns firing. The smoke billowed through the trees, a purplish-blue with undertones of blood red.

Johanna worked as a person possessed. Out came the precious chairs, the bedding, the cradle Christian had made, the cot, also his work. She ran in and out of the house carrying clothes, pots, pans and other household items, and dumped them in a heap on the road. Oh, God. Won't they be here soon – that helper with the horse and cart? She was struggling to push, pull and drag the sideboard out of the house when she again heard the sound of hoof beats.

No, it was not the unknown helper. Lars and his exhausted horse had returned.

'Quick! Climb up here,' he said with an air of authority. 'Here, in front of me.' Johanna hesitated . . . The spinning wheel . . . Martin Luther on the wall . . . the big table . . .

'Hurry up! Stand on that sideboard. Take my arm.' The horse pranced sideways, nostrils flaring as it edged its way towards the sideboard. The Bible! Johanna managed to get the heavy book from the top drawer. A moment later, she was in front of Lars, her right hand buried in the horse's mane. Her left hand pressed the Bible to her chest. Reassuring arms held the reins from either side of her waist.

They heard, rather than saw, a big tree toppled by the storm. Perhaps the roadwork had weakened its roots and perhaps it had been caught by other trees and had only partially fallen at that time. Thank God, it did not block the road. The horse needed no urging. The frightened animal galloped towards safety once more. As they reached the hillock overlooking Lower Norsewood, they met the full force of the storm – heat laden with red-hot sparks like tiny stars. They could see men running in and out of houses, waving their arms and shouting to each other. Perhaps they were checking to ensure the inhabitants were gone?

There was no one outside Berte's house. And not a soul inside either. Oh, kind Jesus – the children! Where are they?

Her alarm lessened when she learned that most people had already escaped, the women and children having gone first. The school had been closed when the risk to the town was realised. However, as many children could not reach their homes, the whole group had been mustered and taken to the apparent safety of the clearing between the school and Kopua.

Other refugees, including Berte Maria and all the children in her care, had accompanied the school children to the Te Whiti Clearing. Still more people had escaped down the Danish Line to the imagined safety of Ormondville and Makotuku.

'No danger there,' a man assured her about Te Whiti Clearing.* 'Safe as churches! Well, not Norsewood's churches perhaps!' He wanted to take off, but Johanna restrained him.

'Oh, yes. Pastor Reis took command. Didn't even try to salvage his own things. Mr Wolstenholme, the teacher, brought his horse and cart too, and the mail coach and they began shuttling to get people to safety. Hurry, there's the pastor now!'

Look! Oh look! A shower of sparks had exploded above Upper Norsewood. The school was ablaze.

---

* Primary sources used here include reports from the *Hawke's Bay Herald* and the *Waipawa Mail*. Key reports were reprinted in A. L. Andersen's *Norsewood: the centennial story* (1972, reprinted Nelson 1997) and *75th Jubilee, Norsewood School 1874-1949* (Dannevirke, 1949). Note that the latter book contains the only source of the key article HBH 19/3/1888, which had been cut from the newspaper before microfilming. Although not stated, evidence suggests that the school children probably escaped down the main road to Kopua Road, as access to Lower Norsewood may already have been blocked at that time. VB.

'Please God, Jesus too! Save Norsewood! Don't let Norsewood burn.' A silent prayer from still lips.

But God did not hear her. And it was already too late.

By the time the town disappeared from view, the firestorm was already well beyond Lower Norsewood. The Lutheran Church was ablaze and next door, the last flames flickered from what had been the pastor's house.

In his younger years in Wanganui, Alex McCallum, grandson of Johanna and Christian, was a policeman and a fireman. He has helped extinguish a wide range of fires: 'Even so, nothing I have taken part in could compare with what Grandad encountered. Burn-offs were essential in those days. It was the only way to clear the land and make farming possible. The best timber was taken first of course, and sent to the mill. Everything else had to be felled, then burnt a few months later.'

Alex went on to explain that there was quite an art to having a successful burn-off. The day must be fine with no wind and there must be the right mixes of light material and logs. The timber must be neither too wet nor too dry. The secret was to have a slow burn – lasting for weeks if possible – and not to generate too much heat.

'Big roaring fires – of course – tend to create wind.' Alex looked perturbed. 'If there was a breeze for a start, there could soon be a gale blowing – and next we have a full firestorm. Burning fragments would fly ahead of the fire front, like armed scouts well forward of the main army. I can just see Grandad the day of the big fire. There was nothing he could do to stop it. Poor old Grandad.'

Christian felt so helpless. Lars and the other two riders had set off to try to warn Norsewood of the danger they foresaw. Would they get through that ocean of smoke – the grey, angry, red-lined waves driven ahead by the storm? What would they find on the other side? Would Norsewood already be burning? Had their fifteen years of hard work already been turned to ashes? He conjured up vivid images of the possible fate of his family and home. Were Johanna and the children safe? Where might they be? He needed answers and he could not wait.

It was like the flood of March 1880 all over again. Eight years, almost to the day. That time a cyclone and its torrents of water had prevented him from reaching his family. This time it was a firestorm. If only more horses had been available, but even horses became dangerous and unpredictable when they feared for their own lives. And Christian was not a very good rider at the best of times.

With Lars and the others gone, Christian and the remaining mill workers returned to their whare adjoining the sawmill. However, work and relaxation were cast aside with the axes and saws, as the men focused on far more serious thoughts. Anders was silent. How had his Christine fared? Would she panic? Would she – could she – save the animals, the house, the children? Gloom came easily to Anders.

Arne muttered under his breath. He quietly cursed the unknown entity that controlled the weather and other natural phenomena. These things had always upset his poor old dog. Faithful old Caesar, his arthritic hind legs now barely able to carry his weight. Would the smoke reach him? His lungs were sensitive nowadays. And the little floating sparks could lodge in his fur. Had his wife even released him from his chain? He paled at the thought of the alternative. She could be so thoughtless and forgetful, that wife of his.

Tension was thick at the mill. We should have left hours ago! Christian knew that now. They had seen columns of smoke and smoldering fires early that morning, but had taken little notice. Such things were to be expected at this time of year.

True, there had been no rain to speak of since Christmas and the ground was dry. Many small burn-offs had been started lately. People were keen – too keen – to take advantage of such seemingly favourable conditions. Anders had felt considerable unease recently. All those smoldering little fires. All those logs glowing red . . .

'Still, there's no wind today. It's been absolutely calm.' Christian's soothing words had also eased his own nagging fear.

The wind had sprung up two hours later. Over and then down the Ruahine Ranges. A warm wind that gathered strength with every second, then around 11 o'clock all hell had broken loose. The breeze became a strong wind in no time – like a kitten changed to a tiger by a witch's wand. What was left of the bush to the east of them had burst into flames.

They heard more than they saw. Trees crashed to the ground – weakened perhaps by the fire and then toppled by violent bursts of wind.

'Let's go!'

They rose as one.

The wind seemed hot well before they finally reached the smoke. It snatched at their clothes and clawed at their hair. They travelled fast, keeping close together. Each man covered his mouth and nose with a piece of clothing or a hand, to make breathing easier. Stinging eyes watered as they struggled to see the path ahead. The men looked with trepidation at a huge untidy rimu. Its unusual shape, resembling a knobbly old troll, had seen it spared by the bushmen. Now ablaze, it leaned dangerously across the track and tilted increasingly with each gust of wind. The ground beside it was also lifting ominously. Should they detour into the bush to avoid it? What hazards would they meet there and would they find the track again?

'Run!'

Fear gave wings to their heavy boots. Stumbling, panting and coughing, they ran towards the fire-spitting old troll, their hearts hammering in their chests. Moments later came a deep sad groan – as if from an animal in agony or perhaps an ancient troll. Then an earsplitting crash as the heavy trunk fell amongst splintering branches and a myriad of tiny shooting stars.

Had they cleared the tree by inches or yards? At the time, they preferred not to know, but the tales Arne told thereafter lost nothing with age.

'There was that big tree falling. Every bit of 100 feet and all ablaze. We saw it coming, both of us, Caesar and I. That was my faithful pig dog, you know. Big as a calf and feared by all the wild pigs in the ranges. I ran like the wind. Like the wind I tell you. Simply flew, outstripping Caesar too. It was like thunder when that tree came down. The ground shook. I think Satan himself sat in that tree. He clawed at my back. Ripped my jacket in many places. A new jacket too, my Sunday best. Almost tore it off my back.'

'Oh, poor dog!' The listeners invariably paid attention as Arne's story turned to battling Satan as well as death. It must have been awful.

'Your pig dog? Remember? He was behind you, you said. Was he crushed to death, the poor thing?'

'Oh, Caesar. Oh no. He sidestepped it somehow. Bounced out of the branches barking with glee. Badly burnt of course . . .' There were many versions of Arne's heroic tale, but the ending was always the same. In the story, the elderly Caesar had not been at home that day. He and his master had reached Norsewood just in time to warn everyone – and no one would ever know how many lives they had saved that day.

'No,' Arne reaffirmed. The faithful old battler had not become one of the district's chained-up dog corpses that newspapers had later mentioned. Not his Caesar!

The smoke was thick and terrain they had known for years was hardly recognisable. When they stumbled across the Swedish Line, they discovered what this morning had been Axel Johanson's house. Embers surrounding its brick chimney still glowed red, and nearby a shed burned fiercely. A charred pig – like so many of its kin that day – lay in what had been its yard, its legs pointing towards the sky.

Please God? They stopped for a moment. Anders vomited. Oh God in Heaven, help and preserve . . . He visualised his home at Garfield as a smoking ruin – the blackened corpses of Christine and the children lying outside. He vomited again.

The smoke had cleared slightly, but the sky glowed red over Norsewood. The grey ocean stretched ahead to the east and south, and far beyond the line of fire. The storm had abated a little. Somewhere out there under the smoke, Christian knew, was his own house. Is it still standing? Had Lars reached Johanna and the children in time?

The little stream at Lower Norsewood provided the chance to wash stinging eyes. Their blackened faces also transformed – at least a little – back to something resembling their normal colour. Christian submerged his whole head, then vigorously scrubbed at his hair. A blackened wasteland surrounded them. Houses had mostly vanished, but for the occasional smoldering wall and – where the former owner was slightly more affluent – a few little piles of buckled roofing iron. Brick chimneys, dotted about the place like naked, hard gravestones, stared accusingly towards the heavens. The fire had not spread evenly though. Some buildings, having survived the initial onslaught, were only now ablaze. Others, remarkably amid the chaos, remained completely unscathed.

Prayers had been offered – repeatedly – for every building that day. But God was apparently deaf on the afternoon of 16 March 1888. Shops, Hans Mortensen's Accommodation House, the smithy, the Working Men's Clubrooms, the Lutheran Church and parsonage, Reverend Nielsen's little home, the school and the schoolhouse, were amongst those that succumbed. What a tragedy! All that would survive in Norsewood were the post office, a small store, the hotel, Mr Pettersen's home, two little shops and the Methodist Church.

❀

A handful of men still ran about in Lower Norsewood, but little attempt was made to extinguish fires.

Had anyone seen Johanna? Johanna and the children?

Yes, they had been seen. Not so long ago – the children about midday and Johanna soon after. All were safe and had been evacuated with everyone else. No! No deaths that they knew of. At least, not so far! The Lord be praised. It seemed perhaps He had looked after His Norsewood children after all. Yet the fire still raged.

Further news quickly followed. Pastor Reis had rescued . . . Pastor Reis had taken charge . . . Organised transport . . . Put courage into faint hearts.

Pastor Reis, a Dane who had taken over Pastor Sass' large parish two years earlier, had even acted as midwife! Well, not quite. While he was burying his precious theological books, he learned Inga Johansen had gone into premature labour with her ninth child and could not move. What's more, her husband, like so many other husbands that day, was away in the bush. Abandoning his house and belongings, the pastor had carried her to his buggy and driven her for miles through the smoke to safety. Her stillborn baby had been delivered soon after. By the time he returned to Norsewood, his house and books were no more.

Still, lives were more precious than books and buildings, so the pastoral buggy continued ferrying frightened people, including the school children, to well beyond the smoke cloud. There the pastor dropped them off with instructions to continue quickly to Te Whiti Clearing. Pastor Reis and his buggy, aided by Anthony Lambro with the Norsewood-Ormondville coach and some other vehicles, frantically repeated this journey with more women and children until the bridge near Norsewood became impassable.

With his church and home lost, the pastor had accepted that what the Lord giveth, He had now chosen to taketh away. Yet, the pastor also knew the good shepherd tended his sheep first and buildings, but not lives, could be replaced.

The pastor still felt a pang of regret for the beloved books that were now merely wind-blown ashes.

There was no doubt as to who was the uncrowned hero of Norsewood! However, others were praised too, especially the three horsemen who rode through the fire to warn everyone. They had also delivered many others to safely, either double-banked on their exhausted horses like Johanna, or, in the case of small children, in their arms.

They stood dirty and ragged in the middle of the clearing, unashamedly hugging one another in front of everyone. Then came the tears. Tears of joy, of gratitude, of exhaustion, and as a cleansing release. Johanna had been sitting on the ground at the far end of the clearing. Little Fredrik was on her lap and the other children were around her. She had leapt to her feet and run towards him, having hastily passed the baby to Carl August. Work-worn hands clasped tired bodies and for some minutes they clung reassuringly to each other. Did she know what happened to . . . No, but did he know that . . .

No, and no again. But they now knew for sure they still had each other and the children – the things that really mattered.

However, reaching apparent safety did not end the danger. The *Hawke's Bay Herald*'s Norsewood correspondent had – somewhat belatedly – joined those who had rushed to what they hoped was the safety of Ormondville: 'Tremendous fires are raging in the bush,' he wrote with urgency. 'The wires are down as I write this (4:15 o'clock), but I think this brief note will get through. I have just arrived here from Norsewood, having had great difficulty in getting through, as the whole place appeared to be in flames. Fires are burning in other parts of the bush, but the gravest conflagration is at and near Norsewood. The country for miles around is in flames, and as a terrific gale is blowing the fire is spreading, with dreadful rapidity.' He added that rain, and a great deal of it, was the only thing people thought would stop the fire. 'The outlook appears to me to be a very grave one unless rain comes and the wind drops.'

Little pockets of Doomsday gloom had developed among the escapees in their various refuges. A great sense of spirituality had manifested itself in some small groups, the members of which were convinced 'Judgement Day' was upon them. What else could have allowed this disaster to occur? What's more, the fire was still rampaging through the district and those who had escaped to the perceived safety of Ormondville soon realised that once again, they were in the path of the flames.

The fire had swept across the German Line – the road some escapees had taken to reach the Te Whiti Clearing. The German settlers living there were now homeless and in some cases possessionless. It had relentlessly pursued others down the Danish Line. It had crossed the railway tracks at Kopua, and licked at the base of the large wooden railway viaduct at Mangarangiora, alongside Ormondville. And its sights were now firmly fixed on Ormondville. Only Mako-tuku, and those who had sought refuge there, had apparently received God's blessing on that terrible day.

The *Hawke's Bay Herald*'s editions of 19 and 20 March, recorded that by 8:30 p. m. the refugees at Ormondville were sure they would be stifled by smoke, if not burnt alive. The gale was now a roaring hurricane, to the extent that pieces of fire the size of men's hands were being blown distances of around 2 kilometres. Meanwhile the smoke – which could not rise due to the wind's intensity – prevented any attempts to save property. Quite simply, no one could breathe near the fires.

God intervened at 9:00 p. m. and the terror of the day evaporated. The heavens had opened overhead and the wind was suddenly still.

Perhaps it was a sign from the Lord that Judgement would be suspended for now. The sins of the settlers – perhaps –

had been forgiven and here was another chance to live a blameless life.

Not a drop of rain had fallen when the great zigzag lightning first tore through the sky. The thunder that rolled and rumbled among the hills immediately thereafter, over-whelmed the sounds emanating from the fire. The echoes had barely ceased before the next lightning streaked through the sky. The small groups that had earlier feared divine retribution now knew they had been right all along. The prayers they offered were loud and urgent

Pastor Reis, though, did not lead them in their sup-plications. His horse was terrified and trying to escape, and the pastor was preoccupied with clinging to its bridle and attempting to calm the distressed animal. The horse was half-blind, like so many other animals and people, from its lengthy exposure to the heat and smoke.

Then the rain came! Not softly and soothingly, but pouring straight down in drenching sheets from the black sky. Was this a waterfall from heaven? Terrified people scattered in a desperate search for shelter while lightning and thunder crashed and rumbled in the skies above. Yet beneath this new terror came, before long, the realisation it was no longer the fire that was illuminating the sky.

Those who had stampeded in panic to Ormondville and Makotuku could adjourn to the hospitality of the Settlers Arms, Makotuku and Beaconsfield Hotels. However, the school children, their mothers, siblings, and those who had joined them at Te Whiti Clearing, were now soaked to the skin in their light summer clothing. They shivered with cold as their hair was increasingly plastered to their soot-stained faces.

Back to Norsewood! The pastor had issued his order and there was a ring of command to what he said. He loaded his buggy with some of the least mobile of his charges, while more clambered aboard the little collection of vehicles gathered there. The long bedraggled caravan, mostly people on foot, sloshed homeward through the pouring rain. Meanwhile the thunder and the lightning played overhead. Some sought shelter in the homes of settlers, but most trudged onward towards the village. And, of course, all were reduced to walking once they reached the partially-burnt bridge.

When the tired, heat-damaged eyes of the returning refugees finally fell upon Norsewood, or what was left of Norsewood, there was a single welcoming light amidst the blackness. Miracle of miracles, the Junction Hotel, that much maligned home of Satan, was still standing! Homeless women and children, and any men who could fit, crowded into the shelter and warmth of the building. Meanwhile, the storm raged throughout the night.

Next morning, the district's refugees awoke to a beautiful calm and sunny March Saturday. However, the reddened eyes of those who could still see soon met burnt trees, blackened chimneys and piles of crumpled ironwork. The fires might be out, but the smell of smoke, dead animals and rain-soaked wood hung in the air. Still, some buildings had been spared altogether and others needed only minor repairs. Thank God for that downpour. A few people wept with shock, but all knew it could have been much worse. Even so, everyone knew the danger was only hidden. Another strong wind could easily reignite the smouldering logs.

Searchers soon confirmed the fire had spread more or less over a triangular area. This stretched between a point about a kilometre westward of Norsewood, another point 1.6 kilometres or so southward of the village, and Ormond-ville. The longest side of the triangle was about 7 kilometres long.

That morning, Pastor Reis spoke briefly to the dejected crowd of the virtues of solidarity and support among fellow man. Christian thought the speech was hardly necessary –

these same actions had already sustained Norsewood for fifteen long, lean years.

Forty families – totalling 170 people – were left homeless by the disaster. Of these, seventeen families, or 68 people, became totally destitute. Furthermore, the eyesight of almost every person and animal in the district had been affected by the smoke and heat, and for a few days, many were blind.

Christian and Johanna had placed their soaking children onto a wagon at the Te Whiti Clearing, but they had walked the whole way back to Norsewood. They were afraid to be separated, but there simply weren't enough wagons available to carry people who were capable of carrying themselves.

'Do you think our house is standing?' It was the fourth time she had whispered the question.

'Yes, yes. I both think and hope it is, but we shall soon know.'

They had been amazed to find the hotel still towering triumphantly above the ashes. It proved to have briefly caught fire three times, but each time the fires had been extinguished. Its stables, though, were gone. That night at the Junction, people slept where they could. Hunger and comfort, in most cases, must wait until tomorrow.

Once more, it had been Lars who had come to the rescue. He had already installed Elsie and their two young sons in a small guestroom at the Junction. Then he invited Arne Shoemaker's family to join them, and now he made room for the Christiansens and their six children. No one had a comfortable night's sleep.

What was the origin of all the mattresses and blankets, clean clothes and other items that began pouring in the next day, both by road and via the railway station at Ormondville? It was a mystery, but it was said that people as far away as

Takapau and Dannevirke had immediately donated every-thing they could spare, and more besides. What's more, rumours suggested offers of assistance were coming in from around the country, and important people were rushing to Norsewood to assess the situation. And the tasty soup? That was no mystery. The Wrights, the Junction's owners, and a great many willing helpers, had stoked up the hotel's big stove and its outside coppers. They had then piled an assortment of meat and bones, and no end of vegetables, into an array of large pots – many of which had been retrieved from burnt homes. Much of this food had been donated from around the district. After all, it was late summer – the season of plenty.

Was their house still standing? As Christian and Johanna prepared to find out, a knock at the door briefly disrupted their plans. Mr Gribble – until only days earlier the town's postmaster – stood there, albeit minus his distinctive homburg hat and the waistcoat that normally accommodated his distinctive watch and its equally distinctive heavy gold chain. Better known as Mr Pickwick, due to his pompous manners and corpulent body, now, without his status and its symbols, he seemed quite normal. In fact, he seemed quite humble. He asked to thank a young man who had helped him the previous day, whom he understood occupied this room.

Lars looked embarrassed.

'Oh, that was nothing. Nothing at all.'

It transpired that Pickwick had lingered so long to lock his premises, that the fire had blocked his escape. Finally, in a state of bewilderment, he lay down on the ground.

'Just to clear my head for a moment – if you see what I mean. A brief rest, then away again to combat the conflagration. And, of course, you must understand that there is less smoke next to the ground.'

And there Lars, or rather his horse, had found him on their final sweep through the town. Variations of this dramatic tale appeared over subsequent weeks, but all included Pickwick's elegant hat being trampled by Lars' horse. Furthermore, they all included the stout gentleman professing to being unable to mount the horse. The popular version claimed that Pickwick, on horseback, had made a triumphant exit from the smoke, waving his hand in the air like a conquering hero – although minus his homburg hat. However, some people knew differently.

The heat and smoke had been so bad by the time he decided to leave, that a stroll down the only remaining escape route was impossible. Confessing his inability to ride, Pickwick had begged to hold Lars' stirrup and run beside the horse. However, about 100 metres from fresh air he had collapsed beside the cantering horse and had resigned himself to death. At that moment, another man ran by, and with his help, Lars had hoisted Pickwick into the saddle. The pair had then ensured the exhausted man did not capsize again as the little band rushed to safety.

It cannot be verified that Mr Gribble offered Lars a guinea that evening for his 'invaluable assistance', as he is supposed to have put it. And much speculation on the extent of his gratitude was to follow.

It was well into the afternoon before they got away. There had been too much to do. Too many people needing immediate assistance with burns and blindness. And they and the children also suffered considerably from dried-out eyes. Carl August had asked to come as well, but Christian was adamant. It could be just too much for a sensitive boy – especially one with more value to the family where he was.

'No. You must remain here and care for the other children. Put them to bed if it gets dark. Your mother and I won't be long.'

Chimneys cast long shadows across the ravaged wasteland. The couple walked in silence, looking carefully where they placed their feet. Many branches and other obstacles lay in their way. Some trees had been stripped naked by the fire. Others appeared completely unscathed. Bellbirds normally sang at this time of day – but not a single note could be heard. The trip to Garfield took longer than usual. Two badly burnt rimu trees now lay across the road. They detoured around one and scrambled beneath the black branches of the other, and soon the grey ash coated their hands and knees. They paused by Anders and Christine's home – now just a chimney and a few iron household items, but their real object of interest was around the next corner. Christian searched out his near-empty tobacco pouch. Chewing even a few fragments might calm his nerves.

With a cry of surprised joy – Thank you God! Thank you! Thank you! – they began running in pent-up relief. Their house was still standing. Standing!

Their joy and relief faded, though, when they got closer. From the pile on the road that yesterday contained their earthly possessions – their chairs, benches, household goods, clothes, handmade quilts, mattresses and dresser – only a few blackened pots and pans stared back at them. No driver had found time to rescue their possessions.

Several dead hens lay near the house. To their surprise, one looked alive on its nest beneath a singed bush. However, its feathers proved to be scorched and its little black eyes no longer sparkled. Johanna gently lifted the dead hen, and jumped back with surprise. Five little yellow balls had darted from beneath their dead mother and were soon twittering around her ankles.

Johanna brushed away a tear. The mother hen had sacrificed her life to protect her babies. This amazing act, by this lowly and often annoying hen, would continue to draw tears for some time to come.

The animals, were they alive? Johanna's thoughts were answered in seconds. A long drawn 'moo' from near the stream indicated that, thank God, at least one cow was alive.

Inside, the house was as Johanna had left it. Her footsteps

echoed unnaturally as she walked from room to room. The building now contained only the big table and the spinning wheel. Thank the Lord for that. And Martin Luther on the wall, who looked at her as sternly as ever.

Johanna and Christian returned to the blackened pots on the road. They could be reused they knew. Dusk was descending and Christian put his arm around his wife's shoulders. 'It could have been so much worse.'

She looked up. Scorched trees with jutting limbs, dead hens, an empty, dejected-looking house, and the necessities of their life, now ashes at their feet. Things looked worse in the twilight. Memories, or should that be ghosts of what had been there, now screamed silently at her.

'I don't want to live here any longer.'

She had said it. Something had broken inside her. She had not meant to hurt Christian, but everything struck her so suddenly she had not held it back. Christian was stunned by the remark, but said nothing and only tightened his arm around her shoulders.

12 A fresh start

'THESE dairy factories have been the making of this settlement,' said the Casual Traveller to me as we stood on the verandah of the Junction Hotel at Norsewood, Hawke's Bay, and looked at the tumbled masses of the Ruahines that served for background to a frontage of well-looking homesteads. The little village looked prosperous enough, and is the most polyglot place of its size and kind I have struck yet.

Between Ormondville, the nearest station, and Norsewood itself, I had come along the 'Danish line', so called because it had been settled by Danes; the road that led off to the right was the German line, having been colonised by emigrants from Germany; the village itself and the bulk of the district beyond had been settled first of all by Norwegians and some few Swedes, 'Skandies,' as the local term is.

The church, large and well kept, is singular for having three services held in it each Sunday. The first for the Germans, the second for the Danes, each of these in the language suited to the nationality, the third, in the evening, is given in English, which all the young people speak as their mother tongue. 'Alfred's laws and Chaucer's speech are theirs, whether they will or not,' as

Dilke says in 'Greater Britain'. You would not think that here was found the model for a dairy factory, yet so it turned out.'

This article in the *Bee and Poultry Journal*, of June 1898, went on to describe in detail the new Norsewood dairy factory, after first describing the novel 'bush landaus' of the area, otherwise known as 'Scandi wagons'.

I don't want to live here any longer. How the words had shocked him at first, but he understood her well. As soon as they returned to Garfield – together with Anders, Christine and their children – he started looking out for something better.

The Junction Hotel continued to provide accommodation for the homeless, many of whom had survived the fire with nothing but the clothes they were wearing. Others found space in spare rooms, or spare parts of rooms that were offered by the more fortunate. Assisting one's neighbours was second nature in the district. They did not need Pastor Reis to remind them of their duties.

Considerable help came from outside the district as well. The Danish and German consuls, and representatives of various elected officials visited the town and issued reports. These emphasised the need for considerable help for the sufferers, including attending to the long-term problems these settlers had endured. The editors of newspapers in Waipawa, Napier, Palmerston North, Feilding, Wellington and in more distant parts of the country, lost no time in calling for donations for the hundreds now in need. Blankets, clothes and foodstuffs were consigned to Ormondville Station for redistribution to the needy. Tools of all sorts – in fact many more than had been lost in the fire – arrived from individuals, community groups and organisations. Cash donations were also received. It was not long before the music of hammers and saws rang out through Norsewood. Reconstruction was in full swing and a song was in every heart.

Many hearts, though, did not eagerly anticipate the idea of rebuilding. The incomes of many people had not stretched to property insurance. And just as Johanna felt the strong urge to leave Garfield, Axel Johanson of the Swedish Line also wanted to move. His German-born neighbour, Robert Müller, felt the same. Both knew plenty of sawmilling work was on offer in the up and coming 'Sawdust City' (Dannevirke), so why not just move there and have done with it? As luck would have it, both wives agreed. The two women were more than happy to encourage Christian in his business endeavours. To Johanna and Christian's relief, even the bank apparently considered Christian's prospects for the future to be reasonably good.

First things first though. The Garfield property needed to be disposed of. Anders and Christine, now homeless, quickly – and eagerly – noted the situation. Here was a God-sent chance to double the size of their farm, and once again possess a house. If only . . .

'We did without many things all these years, but we always paid our insurance fee – just in case . . . And our house was insured for £150! When that's paid out – any day now – I'll give you that for your farm. And another £100 that we've saved. Aren't we lucky we hadn't saved it under our mattress? It will be in cash too. Yes, it's a firm offer.'

This was big business. Christian thought hard. He had always wondered why Anders and Christine had seemed to be so poor, when he knew how much Anders received and how little was wasted. It was really serious stuff though. To tender for a block of bush was child's play compared to this. The furrow across his brow grew deeper. A small pinch of tobacco was needed. It was a fact, though, that the house was still fairly basic, and it would need replacing before long.

'£250 in cash and another £100 to be paid over the next two years? You know Garfield is starting to develop in its own right, and there's even talk that the Larsens' plan to build a hotel across the road. And who knows Anders, perhaps some day there will be a little village on your doorstep?'

'Done!'

'It's a deal.' They shook hands, both containing their delight at their respective bargains – and their perceived business skills. It had all been so easy.

Their wives, who had pleaded for a simple settlement, had really done the mental spadework. Both women knew perfectly well who the real farmers would be in the years to come.

Johanna thought, what was that saying about clouds having 'a silver lining'? Was it simply those words from her childhood? *Aldri så galt, er godt for noe* – no matter how bad, something good will come out of it.

Surely that applied to the Norsewood fire. Tragic though it was, no lives had been lost. No human lives anyway. And all sorts of good things had flowed from it ever since. God moves in mysterious way, Pastor Reis had said more than once . . . Well, yes. Johanna could see the Lord's hand in this too. Up to this stage, it had bothered her that the Lutheran Church had been destroyed, while the hotel had been spared. The house of sin had survived, while the house of God was just cinders on the ground.

The logic of this had concerned her. Yet the hotel had provided so many people with shelter when they desperately needed it. Therefore, surely God must have remembered that His house lacked beds and cooking facilities. Of course! God must have saved the hotel to help the poor people who had lost everything.

The deal with Axel Johanson was quickly sealed. There were no buildings left on his farm and the 40 acres of good land could be Christian's for £200. Little pondering was needed for this decision and only the smallest pinch of tobacco was needed. Christian was well informed. Back then it was standing bush, but now it was mostly cleared, although it was dotted with badly charred stumps. Axel had not worried too much about stumps, and there were theories that his bush burning talents left a little to be desired as well. Still, underneath was first-class land.

'I shall be happy to accept.'

The many handshakes had been followed by the appearance of a dangerous-looking bottle. Axel proudly announced it contained genuine Swedish schnapps. A sale must be sealed with a dram. Axel was adamant on this point – and good Swedish customs were to be upheld. Christian's initial hesitation – he had avoided alcohol for some years and had almost forgotten how to say *Skål* – gave way to the importance of the occasion.

It was just a thimbleful. Just a wee thimbleful. Only one. In his confession to Johanna, he chose not to mention the wee dram had gone down very easily. Or that it had warmed its way through his heart – and right down to his stomach. Axel Johanson was such a likeable fellow and so easy to do business with. Christian wished the whole family every success in Dannevirke.

Robert Müller proved a harder nut to crack. £400 for the lot – the farmhouse and land. Not a penny less. Surely that was a little steep? The fire had consumed the other buildings on the property, but the house was nice. That was true. Well-built, quite big, an upstairs attic containing two extra bedrooms, and with a verandah on two sides. The children would love that . . .

'£300?'

Robert shook his head.

'£350?'

Robert still shook his head. Christian stood up and prepared to leave. He could not afford to go over that figure. Then Frau Müller stepped in and displayed the quality of German steel. First, there was a whispered conversation with her dear neighbour, Frau Johanson. The ladies wanted to move to Dannevirke – straightaway. They were sick of backblock living – even by Norsewood standards – and the hand-to-mouth pioneering life. She turned back to her husband. The whispering became louder '. . . *dass du akseptieren willst*. No one will make you a better offer . . . *in diesem Augenblikk. Ich dir flehen,* Robert.'

Robert relented – but not with good grace. There was no shaking of hands or offers of German schnapps. Herr Müller was annoyed. He sensed a conspiracy. Everything must be in writing, but before that an independent witness had to be found. Independent! Robert stressed that word. When dealing at the same time with several opponents, one had to be vigilant. Pastor Reis signed all three copies of the contract. Christian was to pay £250 immediately and the remaining £100 in four instalments over the next two years.

Christian and Johanna stood together on the verandah of the Müller house – their house! Eighty acres! All in one block, and all on the western side of the Swedish Line. Good land too, reasonably flat and slightly tilted to the northeast. Some pockets of bush remained, some scorched and ravaged by the firestorm and other parts left untouched. Almost all the logs on Müller's farm had gone. There was room for many milking cows, not just the three – and the other assorted livestock – they had brought with them from Garfield. No, they could start to think about dairy farming in the future and not just about trying to grow vegetables, mutton, wool, grain and endless grass seed. At least they could do this, if all the talk about butter factories ever came to anything.

Johanna wished her poor dead father had lived to see this. It was just what he had dreamed of back at Pasotorpet. 'I'll bring Mother and Julius up here on Sunday. It will mean a lot to her. I hope Grandpa can see us too. Old Paso would be so glad.'

Good years with heavy work had passed. A few months after moving in, Johanna gave birth to son number six. He was christened Martin. Then followed Daniel William and two years later, Arthur. In the summer of 1894, Sarah Elizabeth arrived, followed by Eva Maree two years after that. Eighteen months later, another boy, Enoch, was welcomed into the world. No more children, Johanna said. She was now 42 years of age.

God gave us thirteen children, and twelve are alive and well. That must be enough. Christian understood and agreed. Enough was certainly enough. He could also see Johanna's strength slowly ebbing. With the strain of farm chores and constant maternity, she was no longer as sprightly – or quite as tolerant – as she once was. Should he retire from bush contracting and become 'just' a farmer? Not just yet. Soon, perhaps.

Just before the century ended, tragedy struck. It was his fault – his, and his alone! Johan – his very special son – who was meant for something great in the world . . .

Christian had entertained the same dreams for Carl August too. However, Charlie, as everyone called him, had turned out differently. There was no doubt God had bestowed many gifts upon him. He could be light-hearted, clever and witty, but he was also a thinker and melancholy thoughts were never far from the surface.

Charlie seemed unable to settle at anything. Not at work in the bush . . . Not at prayer meetings at home (he would creep outside). He did not involve himself in the Salvation Army, when that became dominant in the family's life. No again, not the least bit interested, in spite of his ability to play any of their musical instruments.

'What will happen to our boy, and where is he heading?' Johanna would sigh deeply. 'He is so different from the rest of us and does not show the proper respect for Our Lord either. He is like a ship without a rudder.'

Charlie had worked in the bush with his father since he turned 14. He never complained, but it was obvious he had no love for the axe and saw. When the chance arose, he tried to shorten the tedium with a little merriment . . .

Lars did not laugh, though, when he and Charlie were set to deal with a particularly large matai log with a radius of around two metres. Each struggled with his end of the crosscut saw – unable to see the other. Lars noticed the work grew harder and harder, and slower and slower. Finally – having concluded the matai's core was made of iron – he released the saw to wipe his brow. How was the young fellow doing on the other side? Worn out and as tired as he was? No, he was lying on his back, arms behind his head, gazing at the clouds with a grin on his face. Oh, the lazy devil!

When he was 18, Charlie farewelled the bush for good. However, Johan, at 16, was by then a fully-fledged member of his father's contract team. He was keen and interested – and a solid young worker. Christian dreamt that perhaps a few years hence there would be a Christiansen family bush gang – including Joseph and Rolf – but he made no attempt to stop Charlie from leaving.

And Charlie left. He found his place at the Huiarua Station at Tokomaru Bay. There he, his horse and his dogs cared for peaceful sheep. So much better than toiling in the bush, where strength was essential and competition with the others was constant – even if not acknowledged. Still, packing and leaving had been surprisingly difficult. He felt a strong bond to his family, especially his mother. This was despite feeling she smothered him with all her religious talk, now she was a devout Salvation Army member. The need for a guiding star . . . The straight and narrow path . . . He couldn't take any more of that!

'Don't worry! I'll be back soon.'

Carl August did not come back so soon. And when he did come, the family saw little of him. Usually he took a room at the Crown Hotel and met his friends there. He had many friends as it turned out. It was easier that way and it meant he did not bother his family.

His parents knew though. They knew he drank, that he kept bad company and threw his money away on friends not worthy of the name. Yet Charlie remained kind and generous towards his family. His siblings knew to expect presents when he visited and he never failed to push a pound note onto his mother. Occasionally a box of groceries also appeared, while an envelope containing his fare back to Huiarua was also invariably placed into Johanna's care.

Johanna could not understand her son. She valued his thoughtfulness – he had always been kind-hearted – but he was a mystery to her as well. 'What can we do to make him mend his ways?'

Christian could not give an acceptable answer, so replied in a lighter vein. 'He is still young. This is something he must get out of his system. Let's be patient. He will come to his senses one day.'

That was of little comfort to Johanna, he knew that. Yet to start arguing or being dogmatic about spiritual matters, well, it did not help. Johanna prayed that God would speak to her prodigal son in His own good time, but continued to feel a sense of unease.

Christian and Johanna were unaware that Charlie wrestled with his own problems. He thought even Martin Luther could not have struggled more intensely in his search for truth. But as there was no one Charlie could talk to, he kept his thoughts to himself.

Was he truly a disbeliever and a fallen soul? No, he did not think so. But his God was faceless and shapeless, with no gender or personality. His God did not even have human characteristics. Had, instead, we all shaped God in our own image? Charlie had been told so many times that it was the other way around. The Bible also said 'God is Good,' and surely that was the same as 'Good is God.' He found this thought comforting. Still, Charlie felt alone. Even when staying at the Crown Hotel surrounded by friends and with laughter ringing in his ears.

His confusion seemed to trace back to the weeks surrounding the big fire of 1888. He was only 10 then, but had watched and listened as the lives of so many people had been turned upside down. He had been intrigued by Reverend Nielsen's angry remarks. These were published in the *New Zealand Methodist*, but Charlie had read them after the *Daily Telegraph* reprinted them. Johanna had preserved the clipping, which was dated 25 April 1888:

> *With regard to the cause of the fire, I look upon it as a judg-ment from God for the wickedness of the people, who refuse to repent after hearing so much of God's Word, although thank God there are a few God-fearing people there. About four years ago the Norsewood people by their own votes closed the hotel in the township and three others in the district. Only a week before the fire the people voted to open the hotel again, and did so with much joy. If others cannot see, or will not see, God's hand in this calamity, I can see it, and I know the people well, having been acquainted with them for thirteen years. May the visitation be a warning not only to Norsewood, but to the whole colony.*

The article had generated much discussion and considerable heat in various church circles. Did Reverend Nielsen suggest that the God-fearing group in Norsewood were the members of his own little Methodist flock? The 10-year-old's curiosity had also seen him note the concluding comment by the *Telegraph*'s editor. This unknown person had added: 'Yet the church was burnt down and the pub escaped.' That editor, of course, hadn't realised that although the Lutheran Church certainly burnt, the Methodist Church was still standing.

Which side was God really on? Carl August knew there were several Christian denominations in Norsewood and many other denominations and indeed other religions in the wider world. Did they all claim God was on their side? Did they say they had seen the light and that all the others lived in darkness?

Perhaps it was a bit like the sun? What the new teacher

had told the class the previous week about the sun and all the sunbeams. Sun rays, he called them. There were masses of them. Some struck some people and others struck other people. Did everyone think only he or she got hold of the right sunbeams? Did they not know that all the rays came from the sun anyway? Could the churches be a bit like that? All grabbing their own little bit of truth? And thinking they had everything?

It was true the people of Norsewood had voted only days before the fire for a new Licensing Committee. It was now filled with people who supported licensing hotels. Four years had elapsed since the Edwards murders, and only the Junction Hotel remained under the Norsewood Licensing Committee's control. Within weeks of the fire, the Wrights had advertised that they would apply for a new license for the Junction. Englebret Olsen, who wished to license a new hotel in Upper Norsewood, joined them. His new hotel, he announced, would be named the Crown. And of course there were the Larsens who, for just a few weeks, considered establishing a hotel at Garfield.

Carl August and the other Norsewood children were even taught in the Junction's large rooms for many weeks, as they waited for the school to be rebuilt. After the licenses were approved, they watched the major redecoration that occurred at the hotel as its owners anticipated an equally major upsurge in business. As other families struggled to put even the most simple roofs over their heads, Carl August had also watched the Crown quickly take shape. The children's lessons were moved to private homes several days before the Junction's big reopening on 2 July 1888. The incomplete Crown had opened several weeks later.

Christian was proud of Johan and Josef, who was two years Johan's junior. Both were true sons of the forest. They enjoyed their work and their father's company, and were always cheerful and open. They practised their music all week and were key members of the Norsewood Salvation Army Band. Johanna was also very proud of them. If only Carl August could be like them.

Johan was interested in everything associated with the bush. As a schoolboy he had accompanied his father to his contracting jobs. Not to work, but to gaze and admire. This interest had continued when he joined his father's contract team. The summer of 1898-1899 had been especially exciting. Work had started on the new road over the Ruahine Ranges between Norsewood, and Apiti, overlooking the Pohangina Valley. When completed, the journey between Norsewood and that district would be a mere 19 kilometres.

Apiti was a new settlement, but people thought it would have a bright future. At the Norsewood end, the road was merely an extension of Ngamoko Road. It climbed a spur behind the sawmill at which Christian's team was now based. These were hectic days with many people coming and going. This was in addition to the constant inward flow of logs on the wooden tramline, and the outward flow of sawn timber bound for the railway. Johan enjoyed the hustle and bustle. Engineers planned bridges to span the streams and deep rivers that dotted the new road. Surveyors marked and altered ideal routes with pegs, chains and other strange equipment. He particularly noted the theodolite, without the constant use of which the roadwork evidently could not proceed. How did these gadgets work? Could he also learn this skill?

The constant activity on the new roading project resembled a Saturday evening in Norsewood. People roamed about. Loud voices called for various things. And of course, there were the horses, the shovels, the scoops and the wheelbarrows. The workers seemed young. Some had only been youngsters at Norsewood School during his senior years there. All were too busy to talk to him. Many men had come from outside the district. They all slept in big tents at the bottom of the hill and ate from their own camp kitchen.

There was something exciting about all this activity, especially where it involved surveying skills. Johan wondered if he should ask if there are any jobs going. However, before he got around to it, the project began winding down. The people with the money were now concluding that the task was too expensive for the benefits it would gain. Many years would pass before a new purpose would be found. It would be a walking track across the Ruahine Ranges, the Pohangina Valley end optimistically bearing the name Norsewood Road.

One time, and only metres from the new road, Johan noticed a pair of huia. They showed no fear of him, as he watched them pecking away at a putaputaweta tree already dotted with holes. Did they take turns to dig out the grubs? They reminded him of his parents sharing their duties in the vegetable garden. Johan had many questions.

Yes, Christian had seen huia before. Not recently though. Yes, they certainly appeared to be becoming scarce. He felt uncomfortable whenever bird talk cropped up. His favourite, the bellbird, was also becoming scarce. True, he heard them regularly. The dawn chorus trilled away as if they contained the Salvation Army band in their throats. Still it was not what it used to be.

'I have heard that people are shooting huia.' Christian was on the defensive now. He suspected his own work had contributed towards their demise. He also knew far too many people preferred them as ornaments instead of flying free in the bush.

'Shooting?' Johan could hardly believe his ears.

'Yes. To get the tail feathers – the long black ones with the white tips. Or to stuff and preserve in the safety of glass cabinets.'

Those lovely birds that worked in couples like humans! It seemed incredible. If feathers, why not use hen's feathers and paint them? Johan thought of his mother's hens – Black

Orpingtons and the white . . . whatever they were called. How could people do such things? And what was the point of killing off entire bird species just to preserve them in glass cabinets? Where was the sense in that?

Rolf turned 13 the year Carl August left for Tokomaru Bay. He also showed little interest in the forest, preferring life at home on the farm. They had horses now, and how Rolf loved horses. A hack or two about the place, or the heavier workhorses holidaying from their duties at the contract site, always found chores to perform. And the milk needed carting each day to the creamery in Lower Norsewood.

The community had received the opening of the creamery, in late October 1892, with great relief. This was despite many farmers hesitating initially before casting their lot with the fledgling dairy industry. The would-be founder was Jorgen K. Christensen, a keen young Dane who had previously worked at the Mauriceville butter factory. Yet despite his best intentions, he still needed a certain number of farmers to guarantee to supply the new factory.

Pastor Reis took the lead once again. At a meeting he helped organise in early July 1892, the sixty people present had been told what to expect. They would be paid properly for their milk – or rather for their cream. The skimmed milk left over from the process could then be taken home to feed calves or fatten pigs.

Things had changed quickly in the first few months after it had opened. Much less grass seed, a staple source of income in the district, was cut in the first summer after the factory opened. After initial reluctance by some farmers, soon even the most cautious began planning to replace their sheep with cows. The grass would now become hay to feed stock in the winter. However, grain production was still increasing, and plans to establish a flourmill were being discussed.

After the creamery opened, other cows gradually joined

the Christiansen herd at the Swedish Line. Johanna and the children were soon milking a herd of at least twenty-five in the milking season. Meanwhile heifer calves were being retained as future milking cows, instead of . . . Well, that was the unpleasant side of farming! Still, each cow and heifer was a pet with its own name, and was almost a full member of the Christiansen clan. There were fewer silly sheep about the place too, and their days were numbered.

It was good to have Rolf at home. When the others were in the bush, he was the man about the house – and the farm. He did much of the milking and took the milk to the creamery. He undertook important farm tasks such as fencing and general maintenance, and could always be counted on to be willing and helpful. He was a blessing to have around.

Horses were his life though. Brooms had been his special horses when he was a toddler at Garfield. Johanna always knew he had been off riding to some exciting destination, if her one of her brooms was not in its proper place. She usually found them behind the house. His interest in horses grew with him – and at 14, he broke in his first young horse. Others followed. He was proud of his nickname, 'Bronco'. Most appropriate, he thought.

Rangna was 11 when Charlie left for Tokomaru Bay. She was still at school, but assisted Johanna with domestic and farm chores. Litago, her favourite cow, was as good-natured and patient as her Norwegian name suggested. She never needed a leg rope. Rangna had her special chant for calling the cows. Grandma Randi had taught her to yell: '*Ku Båna, Ku Båna, Ku-u Bå-å-å-na.*' And so the Christiansen cows on the Swedish Line would wander home for milking as willingly as their predecessors had done in Odalen. Not all had Litago's sweet nature. Bella, for example, was fickle and temperamental, and only Johanna could milk her.

They are like us, Johanna would say. They have their own personalities and small peculiarities. We must not force them against their will – and her thoughts drifted back to Carl August.

Jorgen Christensen, who had initiated the dairy factory proposal, had soon entered into a partnership with Leonard Andersen, of Norsewood, to become the proprietors of the butter factory. Leonard brought into the business milk-processing skills gained in Denmark and Germany. However, Pastor Reis had been the driving force behind the scheme's acceptance.

The Norsewood Creamery was only a small concern. Only the second butter factory on the Seventy-Mile-Bush (after Mauriceville), the best it could deal with was up to 700 gallons per day. Still, at first, it received a mere 200 gallons per day. By mid-January 1893, though, 500 gallons was arriving daily. There was even talk of establishing a larger factory on a better site to accommodate the growing local interest. The *Hawke's Bay Herald*'s Waipawa correspondent noted at the time, that with the factory in full work, 'the circulation of plenty of ready money is already having its effect in that picturesque village.' Also evident 'in the early morning . . . was a great throng of vehicles of the most primitive types at the factory, waiting their turn to discharge their milk.'

Separating the cream from the milk took time, and suppliers – unless they were early – seemed to wait for hours to bring their skim milk home. Delays or otherwise, there was no doubt the settlers were proud of 'their' big new separator plant. Imported from Sweden, it was steam-driven and perhaps a little temperamental. Maybe it was just that the operators needed time to master the new machinery?

'Shall we bring the skim milk back?' Carl August held the reins on this important first trip to the new creamery. They had two shiny new ten-gallon cans from the Junction Store in the back of their Skandi wagon. They had even paid an extra sixpence each to have the little brass nameplates the storekeeper had been offering, attached to the cans. That way they would know which were theirs when they collected them from the factory.

'Of course. How else can we make *pultost**? Johanna wore her Sunday best today, but with a red kerchief and the brooch Fredrik had given her that first Christmas in New Zealand. This was a day to celebrate. A day to see and be seen.

Danish, Norwegian, Swedish and German flags flew over the new factory behind the Lutheran church in Lower Norsewood that day. People from around the district had joined those supplying milk to witness the big occasion. And Mr Webber had apologised about the Union Jack. They had been unable to borrow one, but it would be flying with the others before long.

Skim milk posed quite a problem at other factories. It was difficult to measure out the right quantity to return to each person. Some would feel they had been short-changed, and the resulting harsh words meant that sometimes the atmosphere by loading docks might not exactly be sweetness and light. Pastor Reis came to the rescue once more. Why not raise the price of the milk from two and a half pence per gallon to three pence? Then whoever wants skim milk can buy it back for a farthing per gallon.

What a simple solution! Johanna had great admiration for a practical person. As it turned out, people had more use for cash than skim milk, and suddenly this waste product was of less value. What would happen now? Was the creamery to be left to drown in it? Pastor Reis had an answer for that too.

'I'll buy whatever is left, and it doesn't matter if it's a few days old. It's for my pigs.' His stipend had been reduced after the 1888 fire, and he had supplemented his income by becoming a pig farmer. Johanna, with her views on eating 'unclean' pigs, found this a little ironic. However, the good pastor knew more than just how to save souls.

---

* A cheese not unlike Feta cheese, but made with caraway seeds.

Johanna enjoyed the occasional trip to the creamery on the milk run, especially when the weather was good. She caught up with old friends and neighbours she otherwise saw only briefly at church or other community functions, and at these times there was often not much time to speak. There was a jovial atmosphere in the town these days. Easy banter passed between people who now had the time to linger and exchange news. Who was ill, who had a new baby, how the children were doing at school, and who had enlarged their dairy herd. Happenings, family events and sorrows – everything had to be shared. It was still a close-knit community.

The trip back from the creamery, along Ngamoko Road to the Swedish Line, was always pleasant. Admittedly, the cemetery was on this route, but even that usually drew only a tinge of sadness. The paddocks were much greener and tidier than they had been a few years earlier, and rotting stumps were diminishing in number. Many farm animals grazed in the paddocks – cows of all colours, horses of various types, sheep and even goats. Straight ahead were the Ruahine Ranges, as dark green and as solid against the polished blue as always. And Christian would be home from the bush on Saturday morning. Only two more days to go.

Karen, Johanna's youngest sister, lived in Norsewood. She had married Gustav Ludvig Winger, known as Ludvig, who had arrived as a young child on the first *Høvding* voyage. The Wingers, in turn, were close to the Jacobsen family, whose wife and mother, Teoline Jacobsen, had died so tragically in July 1885.

People shuddered at the thought of what had happened to Teoline. No one could forget it completely. Everyone knew that any mother in Norsewood could have fallen victim to the same thing. What incredible distress she must have suffered that freezing night. She appeared to have gone around in circles.

The Jacobsen house, on their Ngamoko farm, was almost

2 kilometres from any other. Jacob Jacobsen, Teoline's husband, had been away, as usual, doing labouring work. So when Teoline went into the bush seeking a missing cow, there was no one to mind her children. She could only tell them they must stay in the house and she would not be long. The following afternoon, another settler, also seeking stray cattle, called at the house. There he found the hungry and distraught children – all of whom were under the age of five.

Over two hundred local people had searched for Teoline that cold winter night. They found her the next morning less than 150 metres from her home. Then, because her body seemed lifelike, many had refused to believe she was dead. Even though the doctor had travelled from Waipawa to confirm it, some days had passed before Jacob would allow her to be buried.

Karen had helped care for the four little Jacobsen children after Jacob sold the Ngamoko farm with its terrible memories. He had purchased a cottage in Norsewood, and poured his sorrows into bush work. As a result, he was often away for lengthy periods.

No, Jacob Jacobsen would not sell the Norsewood cottage. 'No,' he said, repeatedly. 'Where else would I keep my furniture and my things?' Kind people had taken in his children in the meantime, but he must still contribute towards their care.

Karen and Ludwig rented the Jacobsen cottage after Jacob Jacobsen accepted bush-felling work near Pahiatua. He had headed off in good spirits that day in October 1890. He would be back for Christmas.

Then in November 1890, Jacob had suddenly vanished. Vanished! People knew he had sewn money into the lining of his new waistcoat. All of £30, it was said. Hadn't he also recently inherited £100 from his sister in Norway?

Then someone exploring near the remote bush campsite where he had last been seen, chanced upon some bones in a hollow rata tree. Some were sheep bones, but others appeared human. Some buttons and metal parts from boots were discovered in the remains of the fireplace. Now, just where was that young man who was Jacob's workmate at the time of his disappearance?

The police eventually him found in Australia. William Joseph Smith, alias Aldridge, was extradited back to New Zealand to stand trial. However, although he still had what was thought to be Jacob's jacket, waistcoat and other items, the charge was dismissed on the second day of the April 1893 hearing. The judge 'did not think there was sufficient evidence to send the case to trial'.

Many things happened in the 1890s, and sometimes Johanna felt things crowding in on her. She burnt with indignation when she read the judge's words, yet she knew there were grounds for doubt.

How do we know for sure those were Jacob Jacobsen's bones? Do we even know for sure he's dead? What if they had hung this man and Jacob's bones showed up in the bush? Remember, just like that lame man, Johannesen? His bones were found in the bush at Umutaoroa (near Dannevirke) last winter, ten years after he had vanished from Norsewood!

People felt rather guilty about that. He had no family in Norsewood and was not very bright. He simply moved around staying with different settlers and did odd jobs to earn his keep. So when people didn't see him for awhile, they just assumed he was staying with someone else. The sad news had so reminded Johanna of poor Old Paso and that well. And, she knew those bones, scattered about by foraging animals, could just as easily have been Christian's.

Other national issues concerning justice pushed the Jacobsen court case aside. Above all, two questions engaged Johanna fully. Should women have the right to vote? And then, of course, there was the vexed question regarding the sale of alcohol.

Johanna felt strongly on both issues, and knew they were linked. The second one was dependent on the first.

'We must get people into Parliament who will listen to us – and who will speak for us. We need people who will close down the pubs. People who will take away licenses to sell alcohol . . .'

Her listeners, usually just her sisters, were in full agreement. And when it came to who should have the right to vote, well, it was as clear as daylight. Of course, women should be able to vote. They were the farmers at Norsewood, and throughout the Seventy-Mile-Bush, and beyond for that matter. They were the day-to-day decision makers. They knew what was best for families, and for society as a whole! Perhaps the question should really be whether men should have the right to vote?

Women from the Norsewood, Ormondville, Makotuku area took a close interest in the 1892 and 1893 Women's Suffrage petitions. The 1892 petition contained 20,274 signatures, including 19 from the Norsewood district. One of these was Johanna's. It is the only known example of her signature.

However, the 1892 Electoral Bill was thrown out by Parliament. Work, therefore, began on an even larger petition to be presented in 1893 – which was, coincidentally, also election year. The organising body nationally was the Women's Christian Temperance Union (WCTU).

However, Johanna's name is missing from the much larger Norsewood contingent (some 31 women) that signed the 1893 petition. Another 46 women from Ormondville and Makotuku also signed. Randine signed both petitions. Containing 31,872 signatures, the 1893 petition had been signed by just under one quarter of all New Zealand's adult women. This time, on 8 September 1893, the Legislative Council passed the Electoral Bill. The Governor, Lord Glasgow, in signing it into law on 19 September, emphasised the point that a woman had in fact headed the British Empire for over half a century. New Zealand, thus, became the first country in the world to grant its womenfolk the vote. And the election was to occur only six weeks later . . .

It was the men of Norsewood – or at least some of the more community-minded of them – who had encouraged their womenfolk to assert themselves in this manner. Did they remember the teachings of Marcus Thrane?

Norsewood's Lutheran, Anglican, Methodist, Salvation Army and Gospel Temperance Union members had held a picnic at Pastor Reis' place in Lower Norsewood on 3 April 1893. There, while the children played, speakers from the various groups spoke of the Temperance Movement's goals.

Finally, Reverend S. J. Wills had proposed a resolution: *That in the opinion of this meeting the women of this colony should be placed on an equal footing with men, and that a bill giving localities the right to suppress or control the liquor traffic should be passed. This meeting therefore recommends the voters of this district to vote only for candidates for Parliamentary honours who pledge themselves to support such principles.* Doubtless Johanna was present and had delighted in her chance to help see this motion passed unanimously.

Still, when the dream became law, only six weeks remained to the election. Women needed to appear on the Electoral Roll if they wished to vote, and nationally, committees were set up to achieve this. Even door-to-door canvassing took place. It was cynically noted that Elected Representatives who had opposed the Bill, now knew where their best interests lay.

Men appointed by the Registrar of Electors to seek enrolments in Southern Hawke's Bay – as elsewhere – discovered great demand for their services. They also found that many people, male and female, did not fully understand the enrolment forms. What, for example, were to be the women's 'occupations', and were Scandinavian wives whose husbands were naturalised eligible? After all, they themselves had not personally been named on the naturalisation papers. So women's 'domestic duties' became their 'occupation' and, yes, the wives of naturalised men were eligible to vote.

While she may have missed signing the 1893 petition, Johanna (as 'Johanne', the Norwegian spelling of her name) did enrol to vote. She listed her occupation as 'domestic duties'. Her sisters Randine Andersen and Karoline (Caroline) Hopkins are also identifiable with certainty as having enrolled.

And the result? Of the 78 per cent of adult women throughout New Zealand who registered to vote, 85 per cent actually did so. Just under 70 per cent of men on the roll also voted. The Liberal Party became the election's clear winner.

The Pasotorpet girls might argue among themselves, but when it came to questions of justice, they stood together. Similarly, their husbands knew what was in their own best interests – most of the time.

Randine was one of Norsewood's leading lights with both petitions to Parliament. Especially the second one – she had taken it from household to household to allow women who could not come to the hall to sign. She had been embarrassed, though, when she realised she had forgotten to visit Johanna!

Seven years younger than Johanna, Randine had taken a leading role in encouraging the women to register as voters in the frantic few weeks before the first election. And she had reminded them of the candidate selected to receive their support. Randine and her friend Annie Redward had become the district's champion suffragettes, the female firebrands of the local Temperance Society! Randine had stood fearlessly at the political meeting at Makotuku that stormy 18 November, to encourage people to vote for Mr Carlile. Her impassioned speech had ended with a simple appeal.

' He is our man. He will fight for our cause in Parliament!'

Oh that girl! They had applauded her. Got to their feet and clapped – and not just the women. Randine's husband, Anton Andersen (Randi's stepson from Makaretu) was one, also Harry Hopkins, Karoline's husband, and many others.

But would Harry feel the same way next payday? It was suspected he was unkind to his wife, but she never complained.

The early 1890s were busy years, but they were good years as well. Life was more than just hardship and hand-to-mouth existence. At last, there was something to show for all the struggles. Finally, Johanna could shape her own life and that of her family. And had she not played her own small part in shaping the colony's future as well?

True, work in the bush remained hazardous. Accidents occurred every year. People still fell from jigger-boards – and certainly, you threw your axe away quickly then! Sawmill workers could be crushed if trees fell somewhere other than intended. Johanna knew sawmill workers needed eyes in the backs of their heads. Falling trees had wills of their own. They could be snagged or deflected by their neighbours as they crashed towards the earth. These forest giants deserved the greatest respect.

Christian would always retain the horror of 20 September 1899. He watched the tree fall many times. Watched its trunk twist ever so slowly on its stump. He watched it pivot in slow motion until a huge branch was suspended in direct line above Johan. The words of warning had caught in Christian's throat – not that Johan would have heard them. Nor would he have had time to run.

Convinced it was entirely his fault, Christian had chastised himself repeatedly. He had forgotten to protect his beloved son. He had forgotten to see where Johan was. Still, his fellow bushmen knew the dangers they faced daily and Johan was no amateur who needed to be watched. They also respected and understood a grief-stricken father's self-condemnation.

Norsewood's curtains and blinds remained respectfully drawn after the news reached the town. Two days later, Norsewood flew the Norwegian flag in quiet celebration of the twenty-seventh anniversary of the arrival, on 22 September 1872, of its first settlers.

Christian treasured his collection of newspaper clippings on the accident, including the one from the *Hawke's Bay Herald* of 28 September 1899. It stated:

> *The funeral of the late Johan Christiansen, the young fellow killed at Mangaone by the falling of the limb of a tree last week, took place in the Norsewood cemetery on Saturday last, when there were a large number of settlers present. Ensign Aikenhead, of the Salvation Army, conducted the funeral service. Widespread sympathy is expressed for the bereaved parents.*

It was true. Almost the whole of Norsewood, and others from further afield, attended the funeral. Many wept when the Salvation Army band played – minus one of its number, and when Ensign Aikenhead spoke of the beloved and gifted man who had been called home to Jesus so early. After the committal, people embraced the bereft family, and each other, as they tried to comprehend the loss.

Even so, nothing could console or comfort Christian. He remained convinced he was entirely to blame. He lay awake at night for a very long time thereafter, picturing the whole tragic scene. He lost his appetite for food, and certainly for work in the bush. He abandoned his contract at Mangaone – and it was many weeks before he could bring himself to re-enter the bush.

Johanna and Christian wept together in each other's arms on many a night after Johan's death.

As the year ended, people prepared to celebrate the dawn of a new century. However, neither Johanna nor Christian joined in. The grief-stricken couple continued to attend church and the Bible remained their rod of comfort. Johanna felt sure her precious boy was safe with the angels.

'He is together with our Rangna now. I can see them quite clearly. Hand in hand in God's garden.'

Johanna was then in her forty-fifth year and knew she was pregnant once more. 'If it's a boy, we shall call him Johan. And if it's a girl, then she shall be Johanna, even if we call her Hannah for short.'

13 It's a girl!

D ANNEVIRKE, Spring 1985. A journey and a meeting with
Hannah that became the starting point for this book. A small
dainty white-haired lady, 85 years 'young', with sparkling blue
eyes. Very conscious of her ancestral roots and deeply interested
in her family history, she had even written two booklets about it.

'It was Mother who told me. She had so many stories. Later I
wrote them down as I remembered them. Stories about our ancestors and about life at Pasotorpet, Christmas in the snow,
blueberries and animals in the forest . . . About all sorts of things
back in Odalen. She had stories about the voyage out, as well as
about the early days of Norsewood. Oh, life must have been so
hard then.' Hannah sank into deep thoughts. Later, though, she
remarked: 'Do keep these two booklets. You will see why I admire Mother so much.'

I must have decided to write Johanna's story that day. Twelve
years were to pass before I returned to New Zealand and began
my research in earnest. Thank you dear gentle Hannah, for those
books. They were invaluable.

Johanna Elizabeth Olsen died in 1994.

Christian could not remember ever being so agitated. He had left the house when the contractions started. It was unbearable to hear and see Johanna in such pain. He had implored God to look after her. Surely, everything would go well this time. This was her fourteenth child, some had been easy, some not so easy. Moreover, the last birth, Enoch's three years ago, had been very difficult and very, very painful. As painful as this one today? Oh, please God, dear, dear God. Silent prayers did help. She had been in bed almost a week that time, and that had never happened before. Had she ever regained her full strength? No, he feared not. And now? It was his fault for being weak and giving in to the demands of the flesh.

Christian had kept a little tobacco in his pocket for this self-evaluation. Just a pinch or two. It had helped him earlier in the day. Calmed his frayed nerves somewhat, and since then, he had been a little less hard on himself. Now, though, chewing on tobacco just did not work. Even the second pinch achieved nothing.

It was mid-morning, on Saturday, 21 July 1900. Frost still lay on the ground. The Ruahine Ranges – snow-capped above, and perhaps below, the dark green bush line – looked forbidding against the pale, frosty-blue sky. Christian's enthusiasm for snow was long gone, and he had left his gloves behind. Johanna's homespun, home-knitted gloves. Home! What was happening there at this moment?

Randi had arrived three days ago with her midwife's bag. Her timing was always good. She had milked the cows, fed the calves and quietly attended to the domestic chores. Her main task, though, had been to instruct Rangna in the great mysteries of childbirth, for Rangna, aged 16, was to be her assistant. Instructions had taken place in Norwegian, the same words repeated several times. Johanna had stepped in as translator more than once. Her daughter was eager to learn, but had been so very much on edge lately. Perhaps this was not the best time for a crash course in the language.

Now in her seventy-second year, it seemed as though Randi had helped half the babies in Norsewood into the world. A large band of new midwives and assistant midwives had also been built up over the years, thanks to her, yet Randi felt increasingly isolated. Her social circle was shrinking and communication with her own grandchildren was becoming increasingly difficult.

What did she have in that bag? Christian wondered. Scissors and some towels? Yes, he knew that, but was there anything else? What else? He had returned to the same clump of trees several times, as he wandered up the road and down the road. Each time he had stopped and listened. No, no bellbirds singing. Not a single note to be heard. Was that a good sign, or not a sign at all? Could there be a little reserve supply of tobacco in his back pocket? He had come across emergency supplies before.

'Papa, it's a girl!' Rangna shouted as she ran towards him.

Christian fell to his knees on the cold stony road, and thanked the Lord in front of his daughter, his heart bursting with joy.

The christening took place a few weeks later.

'What is the name?' Ensign Aikenhead had asked.

'Johanna Elizabeth,' said the parents, beaming with delight.

The Salvation Army had officially 'invaded' Norsewood in November 1891, and had met with instant success. Most people had opened their hearts and their homes to the newcomers, regardless of their beliefs. Admittedly, at the start, the youthful larrikin brigade made nuisances of themselves. The Resident Magistrate at Ormondville knew just what to do with them!

'Army,' Johanna had first thought with a twinge of fear. She remembered gruesome tales of the Swedish army invading Norwegian territory as far as Odalen. Oh, the things they had done to man, beast – and woman!

Still, this was all so different. It was an army of good people, simple, cheerful and practical people. Their message was straightforward. Helping thy neighbour was their main point, so it seemed. It was all so down to earth. Well, there were these things about sin and coming to Jesus first of all. That could be painful to endure. And no, Johanna could not stand outside the Junction Hotel on Saturday evenings and recite her shortcomings to all in earshot. No, never! Had Captain Andrews – that lovely lass – ever been as wicked as she made herself out to be? Johanna doubted it.

In spite of testifying and putting themselves down, there remained a happy note to the Salvation Army. Their songs were cheerful and they sang like angels. Their band was a joy to listen to, so strong and always creating a festive atmosphere. The speakers, once they ceased dwelling on past misdeeds, were happy as well as humble. Humble. Yes, Johanna thought, perhaps their humility is the key to it all. They were humble, spoke simply and made Christianity seem so simple and straightforward. It was not necessary to be learned in order to understand what Jesus said.

It came to her as a revelation. Jesus had not been a learned person. How could he have been? He was just a carpenter. And what about his helpers? His twelve disciples? No, they were just the same. Just fishermen or peasants with no education. Most likely illiterate too. And Jesus had chosen them. Picked them for their faith and their belief. Simple humble people they must have been. Perhaps very much like the Salvation Army officers themselves.

'Let us join them, Christian. We feel at home there. They are good people and so ordinary. And our boys love the brass band . . .'

Lieutenant Barrable and Captain Andrews had visited Johanna at home, and she liked them immediately. Such warmhearted people, she thought. And they were listeners, not just talkers, and not continuously asking her to repeat everything because of her accent. She admired them too.

They were doers, really capable people. Had they not supervised the building of their own hall, which had been sent up from Wellington and placed opposite the Junction Hotel? Wonderful place for a Salvation Army Citadel! Johanna imagined some battles would be fought with Satan across the road. And then they had moved into their living quarters at the back of the hall, even though the building was incomplete.

They were resourceful women, tackling all sorts of daunting tasks. They had borrowed a horse from a bachelor settler so they could deliver their *War Cry* magazines. However, their new horse came with old habits. It stopped at the door of every hotel they attempted to pass – and would refuse to move on for an hour or so. What did the two 'lassies' do? Did they put the nosebag on the horse and sit in the gig to wait it out? No, nothing of the sort! They went inside, distributed their *War Cry*s and talked to the patrons leaning on the counter.

Still, Johanna did not cut her ties with the Lutheran church, nor with Pastor Reis or Pastor Legarth, who married Rangna and John in 1905.

Pastor Reis had taken the lead once more on the dairy factory front. When the creamery in Lower Norsewood grew too small and out-of-date, he worked hard to establish a modern butter factory. However, unlike the first one, the suppliers themselves would own the new one. When the Norsewood Cooperative Dairy Factory opened in Lower Norsewood on 4 February 1897, Johanna was a shareholder.

Johanna was proud to have this special status and it had not been cheap to reach this position. Oh, no! The price was set at ten shillings per cow, and with twenty-five cows, it had amounted to a princely sum. Still, it was worth it – she part-owned a dairy factory. Did Old Paso still watch over her? Was he aware that all their hard work was slowly paying off? Did he realise they had twenty-five cows and were blessed with twelve children and a farm that could be developed much further?

Thank goodness Rolf helped on the farm. Always helpful and peaceful, and always steady and dependable, but horses – not farm work – were still his first love. The boys returned from the bush each weekend, and lent a hand as well. However, they were busy with other things, with friends and outings and the brass band. Johanna baked in anticipation of their homecoming, but did not ask them to work in return. Christian, though, was always willing, but Johanna knew he had also worked hard all week. He needed to rest when he came home to her. Bush work was, after all, a young man's game.

So, responsibility for home and farm fell on Johanna, and she carried out her duties quietly and without fuss. House and garden, cows and children, sowing and harvesting, and the buying and selling of stock, all passed through her head. How she looked forward to the weekends. Then her family would be at home and they could discuss the week past and the week ahead. And how she looked forward to regaining her freedom again when normality returned on Monday.

Rangna was the first to marry. They were all fond of John, her new husband. His father was Jens Andersen, a highly respected and very successful farmer who lived nearby, who even had a road named after him. Jens gave the newlyweds some land at the northern end of the Swedish Line, and they seemed fated for success. However, consumption felled Rangna at the age of 27 years. Her three little boys were just 5, 3 and 1 when their mother died.

Johanna took this hard. Mama Randi had died in October 1910, then Rangna died the following March. Randi had possibly been the only person left in Norsewood who had refused to learn English. Her latter years had not been easy. She was lonely and had borrowed her old spinning wheel back from Johanna. The spinning wheel still hummed tunes and sang songs that reminded her of the forests of her childhood. However, increasingly rheumatism had gained the upper hand. She had suffered considerably from this affliction before the *Dannevirke Evening News* spread the word: 'An old settler in the person of Mrs Randi Andersen passed away yesterday at the ripe old age of nearly 83 years.'

Her son Julius missed her most of all. Now in his late thirties, he had never moved away from his mother. In fact, he had remained utterly dependent on her. Because of his small size (due his badly bowed legs), he had always faced difficulties obtaining work, but he liked people and needed company. And no, he could not live alone with Mama Randi's animals in the cottage on the Napier Road, just outside of Norsewood. The cottage was sold and Julius moved to a small house adjoining the school. There he could see, hear and enjoy the company of other people, but remained lonely in his heart.

Sarah was 17 when Rangna died. She had lived with her older sister and brother-in-law throughout Rangna's last year. The three little boys – Arthur, Dick and Allan – needed love and care their emaciated mother had been increasingly less able to give them. One day, Sarah had been seated at her sister's bedside, holding her hand, when Rangna had asked:

'Will you promise me one thing, Sarah?'

'Yes. Certainly, whatever you ask.'

'To look after my three boys when I'm gone.'

Sarah stayed on at the farm after the funeral. The little boys accepted her as their mother, and the transition from Auntie to Mama was very short. After two years, she and John married.

Johanna visited Julius as often as she could – usually when going to the shop. People gathered at Ole Ericksen's general store – unless they were a few doors away at the Crown Hotel. The jovial atmosphere always present at the shop encouraged the exchanging of news and the telling of tall tales, and Ole was such a likeable person. Not only that, he was also the local Registrar of Births, Deaths and Marriages, and a Justice of the Peace besides. No wonder people looked up to him. No wonder people had, in all secrecy, collected money for over nine months for a silver tea set. The teapot bore the inscription: 'Presented to Mr & Mrs Ericksen by the people of Norsewood'. That had been back in August 1905.

In spite of the warm friendly atmosphere in Ericksen's store, Johanna did not linger long. She bought her tea, coffee and sugar – to be collected on her return journey – and hastened on to Julius' cottage at the end of the street. She had a *Julekake* in her basket, and Julius was a great lover of *Julekake*.*

How strange! Julius, who was a little simple and childish, so small and bowlegged . . . who found it difficult to find work – except in Ole's store from time to time – was the only one who had mastered both languages. It puzzled her. She knew of no one else who had as good a grasp of both English and Norwegian and who spoke both without a trace of an accent. True, the ones who had come as small children aboard *Høvding* had now mastered English, but it was at the expense of Norwegian. And the ones who had come as adults, had never quite got on top of the new language – with neither words nor intonation.

Julius, dear little Julius, was the exception. Perhaps it was a case of being steeped in two languages early enough. Randi had insisted on Julius talking to her in Norwegian, and in the proper Odalen dialect too. Oh, she had been very strict.

Not so with me, Johanna thought. She had been lax, and had given in early. When Johanna had spoken to her children in Norwegian, they had replied either in English, or in a half-and-half language, that was neither fowl nor fish. She had given up in the end. There had been less and less Norwegian spoken as the children came, and now, with

---

* Similar to raisin loaf.

Hannah, it was only English. Had she promised Old Paso to hold on to the Norwegian language? She was not quite sure now. Still, he would understand. He would know that the young ones so desperately wanted to be New Zealanders, to be part of their new country.

Even so, I have taught them something, or they have taught each other. They all know some words, some sayings and some proverbs containing wisdom. And thank goodness, they can all say grace nicely – although Enoch never seems to get beyond the first line: *I Jesu navn går vi til bords . . .*[*]

They show good table manners too. No one could start eating before grace had been said . . . Nor would anyone dream of leaving the table unless he or she had said *Takk for maten*[†] to her. No, her children were not doing badly. She had not let Old Paso down.

Still, were the big boys spoiling Hannah? In all honesty, Johanna thought, the answer had to be yes. They made such a fuss of their little sister when they came home at weekends. In fact, almost competing to see who could spoil her the most. They took her to band practice, on Salvation Army outings, gave her rides on Rolf's horses, and bought her lollies from Ole's store. There was no end to the attention they lavished upon her. There was no doubt about it, Hannah enjoyed the happiest childhood of all her 14 children, even though at times Hannah herself felt giddy and short of breath from all the attention. And her knees could be so very tired . . .

Spoilt or not spoilt, Hannah did not seem to suffer. She was a sweet, good-natured and undemanding child, who was loved by all and had smiles for everyone. Johanna knew, though, she had given Hannah far less time and attention than she had to her other children. Did Hannah have a favourite among her big brothers? Hmm, hard to say.

---

[*] 'We go to the table in the name of Jesus.'
[†] 'Thank you for the meal' (directed at the hostess).

Well, it would have to be Martin, who was twelve years older. She sat on his knee and listened to his stories, and followed him like a shadow when he was home. Still, Martin was not often at home. He had lived for long periods with Julius and Randi. As a result, his grasp of Norwegian was better than that of the other children. And although the stories he whispered to the little girl on his knee were in English, they were about trolls, gnomes and animals that lived in the never-ending forests of Odalen. Martin enjoyed singing and had learned several of Randi's songs. Hannah's favourite was of a little girl who looked after her favourite sheep – until the day the wolf came. Martin knew all three verses. Such a lovely simple tune too. Hannah could never get enough of that little girl and her sheep.

Martin and Hannah shared a similar good nature. The house was a restful place when he was at home.

But 1913 was to be a year of changes. Sarah and John married that year – Rangna's three little boys would be safe, Johanna was confident of that. And with God's blessing, there could be more grandchildren before long.

The same year, Martin, Daniel and Enoch decided to combine in a business venture. They had saved up money, so why not start up their own sawmill? Why not be their own bosses instead of working for others? It was a great day when they first heard the whirring of their own saw at Makaretu. And they were still close enough to go home for weekends.

Johanna had felt for some time that a change was needed, but it was Christian's decision when he finally made it. He was 63 years old. Heavy work in all weathers had taken its toll. He was increasingly afflicted with rheumatism and his enthusiasm for bush work had long since waned. He wanted to stay home. Perhaps they could clear some more land and enlarge their milking herd? He and Johanna this time – if they still had the strength to do it. Finally, the day came when he found the words to announce these new plans.

'No Christian. It's time others took over.'

He was thunderstruck. 'I have asked the boys and no one is interested. Not even Rolf.'

'Perhaps we should sell it.'

'Sell it? Now that we are so well off!' Did she really mean it?

Yes! Her face showed how serious she was. And he could see more. Oh, why had he not seen and sensed this before? Johanna was tired, and even her back was bent. In a flash, he understood, but still he could not conceal his astonishment.

Poor Christian, dear Christian. He was hurt. How could she soften this blow a little? 'I didn't mean that we should stop farming. Just that we are getting old. Both of us. Perhaps we should find something smaller and easier to farm. So we don't wear ourselves out. We have been on this farm for twenty-five years . . .'

And so they found something smaller, something easier. Just outside Norsewood, on the eastern side of the main road, was Hillside Farm.* The young couple who owned it wanted a bigger and more challenging farm. It was like 1888 all over again, only in reverse. So they exchanged properties, and Johanna, Christian, Hannah, their dog Tike and their five favourite cows, moved to Hillside Farm. The other cows remained behind for the new owner.

Easier days lay ahead for the small household. Hannah did the milking and helped Johanna in the garden. She was still at school and wanted to stay there as long as she could. And, of course, school was now only a stone's throw away with Uncle Julius living next door. Everything was very handy.

Finally – oh, the joy of it – Johanna could concentrate on her garden, her flowers, her wool, her spinning, her wool dying and her craftwork. Her fingers had ached for this chance for years. Could talents blossom again after a lifetime

---

* The house is still standing, and is on the left side of the road as one climbs the hill into upper Norsewood.

of suppression? Could her fingers, now stiffened, worn and affected by arthritis, create anything that would give her a sense of pride?

The old spinning wheel from Pasotorpet soon hummed and sang as never before: 'we have time, we have time – fingers not so bad, not so bad, not so bad . . .'

Christian sat on the verandah, carding wool and resigning himself to chewing gum instead of tobacco! Life was now relatively stress-free and certainly free of wet clothes and long days in the bush. Oh, the contentment of just being at home. Of being close to Johanna and being her helper – despite the chewing gum. Johanna detested tobacco – especially in her home – and had always disliked his attachment to it. Still, could he resist the cravings he had for it?

Johanna was right of course, bless her. She saw things clearly and knew it was better to scale down their farming interests at this time of their lives, than to enlarge the farm on the Swedish Line. No, he was not rich in worldly terms – the dreamed-of big farm had eluded him – but he was rich in a different sense. He had gained peace of mind.

The sawmill at Makaretu got off to a good start, but it was all very short-lived. Daniel was amongst the first to enlist in the army the following year when the Great War erupted. He duly found himself in the second contingent to be sent to France. Johanna felt this deeply. Would she ever see him again? Enoch was next – as soon as he was old enough – but the Lord be praised, the army doctor decided he had flat feet. He returned from camp deflated – albeit to the secret delight of his mother. One son on the battlefield was more than enough.

These years were especially hard for people with 'foreign-sounding' names and accents, and their New Zealand-born sons in a sense fought on two Fronts. The obvious one was against the foes with the guns. The other was to show their own family's patriotism, to the many less distinguishable enemies at home . . .

Josef was in camp, and about to sail for the Front, when Armistice Day, 11 November 1918, finally arrived. Johanna felt God had heard her prayers. Daniel eventually came home, safe and sound, but did not share his wartime experiences. Others from the district also proved their loyalty to King and Country during the war, and twenty-five Norsewood boys remained forever on the battlefield.

14 The diamond jubilee

'THE King sends you hearty congratulations and good wishes on your Diamond Wedding Day.' So wrote King Edward VIII's Private Secretary from Balmoral Castle, to Mr and Mrs Christiansen of Norsewood.

Hannah organised the family gathering in 1936. They all came – children and grandchildren – and many from far away. Mother and Father's Diamond Wedding was to be celebrated in style.

Do you remember ... Do you remember ... They shared many golden memories. Voices echoed from several corners in the big kitchen. The boys were competing for attention.

'. . . the creek I told you about.' Dan's voice was rather loud. 'Where I released trout spawn from the Manawatu River. We had trout galore for . . .'

The captive audience had some difficulty recalling details. Grandchildren were creeping in from the garden. Drama was in the air.

'Oh, they all died, poor things, after the Ngamoko bush fire in 1908. Eels as well as trout. Surely, you remember that?'

'That creek! Of course, how could I forget . . . The one we dammed up and turned into a swimming hole . . . Where Ray lost his false teeth and we searched and searched . . .'

Enoch was holding court by the wood range at the other end of the room, alongside the scullery. He was not going to lose his listeners, who were mainly children. Fresh in from the garden and wide-eyed with interest, they were seated on Johanna's rugs on the floor.

'. . . and she was on fire! Poor little Hannah. Auntie Hannah to you, of course. She was only 5 or 6 then.'

The listeners gasped with horror.

'Your grandmother had told her to be a good girl and stay by the copper and stir the cheese while she went to milk the cow. It must have been Bella, that awful beast that only Mother could milk. She told Hannah to be careful though and keep well away from the fire under the copper.'

'And what did little Hannah do? Oh, you guessed it. She got too close to the fire and . . . Whoosh! Her dress was on fire. A blaze! I heard her scream and . . .'

'Those blessed teeth! How we searched. Emptied our swimming hole. Drained all the water out. Searched in the mud – every inch . . .'

'She had a loud voice, our Hannah. A good little screamer she was. I just leapt outside . . .'

'Martin had a dream that night. Saw the teeth quite clearly, lodged under a stone in the mud . . .'

'. . . didn't dare to lift her up, I would have caught fire myself. I just pushed her over and rolled her . . . over and over again . . .'

'There they were, the next morning, exactly as he had seen them in his dream. And that was the morning Ray, our visitor, was going home on the bus. What luck!'

The listeners felt quite limp. This had been stirring stuff.

It was left to Hannah to explain what had occurred thirty years earlier with the cheese and the copper.

'Such a big job it was. It took many hours. In fact, virtually all day – and you had to keep on stirring the whole time.'

She mimed the story as well. The children's eyes remained glued on her. Were all their uncles and aunties such wonderful storytellers?

'Most of the milk evaporated, and what was left turned a warm reddish colour. Then it was poured into a wooden mould to set. And the taste? Just delicious! We had no name for it, but apparently it was called *Prim* in Norway. I honestly think Enoch saved my life that time. Not much older than me, but he knew what to do. Go and give him a big hug!' And she showed the children what she meant.

Martin had waited for a comparative lull in the verbal storm. He simply had to tell the story, once more, of the great Gold Rush in the Ruahine Ranges. There could be people here today who were not fully acquainted with Arne Shoemaker and his Fool's Gold. A hushed silence had fallen on the audience. Martin was known as a great teller of tall tales.

He cleared his throat once or twice, before starting in earnest on the story. Arne was an old man by then. He had long since given up bush work and farming, but had never given up pig hunting.

'There was this new dog of mine, Arne had said. Caesar-Three! He needed some teaching. Just the finer points of pig hunting that only Arne could teach him. But somehow, something was lacking . . .

'All too true! Caesar-Three lacked yellow eyes that could burn with rage and fury. In fact, he was known to lie on his back so his tummy could be rubbed!'

Arne had returned from one of those teaching expeditions with two stones that sparkled and shone in the sun. They were just about pure gold, he was adamant about that.

'Arne found himself the center of considerable attention. Everyone sought his company, and he enjoyed all the attention. The news had spread like wildfire. Wasn't that so, Dad?'

Martin tried repeatedly to draw his father into the story telling, but Christian could only smile and nod. In truth, he felt he was past storytelling, and his memory was no longer the best.

'Where was it Arne? Where? Where?'

The hero was a little coy on this point. He had moved so fast and ranged over such a large area. Still, the gold had sparkled in the morning sun.

'Oh, it faces east!'

Before long, would-be prospectors were on their way, in carts, on foot or on horseback. All were laden with pick, shovel, gold-panning basin, blankets and provisions. Norsewood's shops did a roaring trade. Surely, it would soon rival the South Island of fifty years ago, or even the Klondike. Within a week, many small fires winked back at night, like glow-worms, from the Ruahine Ranges. Some even appeared in the tussock above the bush line.

The skeptics, though, somehow obtained one of the precious stones. Hmm, it seemed so light! Wasn't gold supposed to be very heavy? The stone was sent to Wellington to be analysed . . .

'Oh, you have guessed it.'

Over the years, the children had scattered to the four winds. Carl August, the oldest, had returned for the jubilee from Tokomaru Bay. Rolf came from Piriaka, Fredrik from Napier, Martin from Owhanga, Arthur from Mananui, and Daniel and Enoch from Ohura. Of the girls, Sarah came from Palmerston North, and Eva from Wanganui. Some had come by bus, some by train to Ormondville, and some in the big dust-covered American cars now parked along the main street. And Hannah – the hostess – was there of course, she lived in the Mariboe house, as it was commonly known.

Only Joseph was missing. He lived far away in Cromwell, however, he sent greetings. He had not forgotten his Mama and Papa.

The telegram from Great Britain's new king had arrived – along with the first guests – the previous day. Its words were recited aloud as each family member arrived. How did King Edward know? What had they, who were once refugees from poverty in Norway, done to deserve such a great honour from an English king?

Hannah was 20 when Danish-born photographer, Carl (Charles) Mariboe, decided to sell his home. The four-bedroom house was very old by Norsewood standards, and had survived the 1888 fire. It was also run down and its large section unkempt, the long-time home base of a frequently absent bachelor. Nevertheless, it was in the very centre of Upper Norsewood, and the land that came with it would allow for a big vegetable garden, fruit trees and a large degree of self-sufficiency. It would be the ideal retirement home for Johanna and Christian. Just ideal, they both thought.

It was not that there was anything wrong with Hillside Farm. No, Johanna had great affection for it. It had a cosy little home with a wonderful view. The brooding Ruahine Ranges were in one direction and a large part of the Seventy-Mile-Bush – now farmland – could be seen to the south and east. What's more, to the north they could also see most of Norsewood. But! Yes, there were two buts! Johanna had to acknowledge them both. And they were becoming more marked with the passing of time.

The house at Hillside Farm was small and it was difficult to accommodate the grandchildren who wished to stay. And of course, the grandchildren were a blessing and a gift, and must not be turned away. The other 'but' was that the tiny valley between the house and Upper Norsewood seemed to be getting steeper.

Both Christian and Johanna now suffered from bad knees – and Johanna's hip was also playing up. So, of course, coming and going over all these hills had become a trifle difficult. The couple knew they could not keep asking

Hannah to do all their errands – the shop, the post office, and conveying messages. No, Johanna felt, that was asking too much of a pretty and popular young woman who ought to be getting married anyway. It really would be easier to live right in the heart of Upper Norsewood.

Christian was fully in favour of the move. Although . . . Yes, he had one objection, and it was of a financial nature. 'How could they live in the Mariboe house without an income? Without money coming in from the cows? Just tell me that?'

Sarah, from the Swedish Line, knew the answer.

'Father, you are 70 years old.'

'Yes!'

'And you know about the Old Age Pension!'

Christian was upset. To live on charity! No, never! Money from the Government and for doing nothing! He recalled Old Paso wandering from farm to farm. The Parish Council paid farmers to look after the poor for a few weeks at a time, and so these unfortunate people moved from place to place according to a set rotation. Besides, the pension was just for poor people and they had some money left from selling the farm.

'Out of the question! Charity! No, not for me.'

Johanna took his hand ever so gently. She knew his dignity was hurt.

'Sarah is not talking about accepting alms, dear. Or anything like that. You paid taxes for years, remember. We paid these taxes so we are only getting some of our own money back in our old age.'

Then Sarah added quite sternly, that even if he did not want this money, then perhaps they could give it to Hannah. The family had felt for some time that Hannah really did need a little financial freedom in return for the considerable help she was to her parents.

Money for doing nothing? Christian was clearly upset. However, deep down he knew Sarah was right. He struggled from his chair. Tobacco was needed – chewing gum would not do for this situation.

Christian knew the Old Age Pension had proved a godsend for many people since its introduction in 1898, as minimal as the sum was. However, he also knew he would have to go to court to apply for the pension and many personal and financial questions would be asked. And why should he, with some money, have to answer them? Still yes, though, regarding Hannah's work, Sarah was indeed right.

They moved into the Mariboe house one sunny day just before Christmas 1920. The farm had been sold, along with the farm implements and all but one cow. Neither Hannah nor Johanna could bear to part with Sybil, who was almost a family member. For some time thereafter, Sybil's days were spent grazing at Hillside Farm. Then, every afternoon Hannah led her home to the Mariboe house. There she was milked, and again in the morning, before being returned to spend the day grazing at the farm. The procession of cow and young woman, twice daily past the school and shops, became a familiar sight in Upper Norsewood.

Sybil was Hannah's cow and it was Hannah's responsibility to care for her, although Johanna still aspired to occasionally do the milking. She still enjoyed the smell, the warmth and the closeness of Sybil, with her forehead touching Sybil's side. The chance to milk gave continuity, a shape and purpose, to Johanna's life. She was back at Pasotorpet, at Garfield, or at the Swedish Line. Sybil, as she contentedly chewed her cud during milking, tied all these things together.

True, Johanna knew many exhausted women who had struggled to make bush farms pay, despite the constant strain of pregnancy, childbirth, breastfeeding and childcare, while their husbands worked elsewhere as labourers to earn money. She knew some said these women – and their children – seemed to be enslaved to the twice-daily need to milk cows, come rain or shine. But how else could many of these families have put food on their tables? How many times had she heard teachers complaining of dairy farmers' children falling asleep at school because of this twice-daily chore? It had even been referred to as 'white slavery'! Johanna acknowledged to herself that many times, in the biting wind and drenching rain, she and her own children had felt the same.

Now, though, with just one, this one special cow, milking was not just a job. No, milking and conversing with Sybil was neither boring nor monotonous, even if the conversation was one-sided! Through this one beloved cow, it was possible to see the whole picture of milk and babies, milking and motherhood. Johanna could see how all these things flowed together, and were as ancient as Eve in that garden . . .

More than milking kept Johanna's fingers active. The craftwork she had thought of and nibbled at between babies and farm work had resurfaced. The copper and tubs in the washhouse behind the Mariboe house were ideal for dying her homespun wool, as well as for making her delicious cheeses. Perhaps Charles Mariboe found them just as useful for developing his photos?

Knotting colourful rugs with intricate designs was her specialty. Especially the diagonal pattern she developed from one she had learned back in Norway, where it was used for weaving garters for stockings. And she rediscovered the pleasure of making *fille-ryer* or 'rag rugs', a Norwegian art form practiced by peasants. After carefully selecting strips of old material for their texture and colour, she sewed them into long strips, which she then wove to create narrow, uniquely coloured floor mats. She was delighted at the response from people when they saw the large carpet she had woven for the dining room. She herself had been especially happy to be free to begin the next project!

Johanna found a ready market for her handcrafts, which helped the household finances. Her rugs and mats also went to neighbours, friends and family – and especially to the sales table at the Salvation Army Hall.

The children did at times question their mother's habit of giving things away. But Johanna had only one answer . . . 'What goes out the back door comes in through the front door.' Hmm. True. Mother never seemed to be short of anything.

Johanna's first loves remained the strongest – spinning, dyeing and knitting. These three flowed together into one satisfying task.

They sat on the verandah in fine weather. Christian would be carding and coming to terms – theoretically – with chewing gum instead of tobacco. Thank goodness, thought Johanna, as she recalled her lifelong distaste for her husband's pet affliction!

The verandah faced west and Christian could keep an eye on the Ruahine Ranges in all their moods. Were the bellbirds still singing there? He knew he had been hard on them over the years as he robbed them of their homes and food. Was it too late to make amends? And so he began hanging lumps of fat in native trees growing behind the house. Perhaps the bellbirds would notice them there.

In bad or cold weather, the couple sat inside – Johanna at her spinning wheel or knitting and Christian carding his baskets of wool. The large circular saw blade that served as a backing plate in the open fire threw out a luxurious amount of heat. It also brought back memories of freedom, the bush and the couple's increasingly distant youth. Wherever they were, they were never far apart. And Christian chewed a great deal of gum!

Hannah remained living with her parents. She had made up her mind, looking after Mother and Father would be her work, and the money from the Old Age pension helped meet her own needs. She was offered work elsewhere, but no. The most tempting offer was from the *Dannevirke Evening News*, which had published articles she had written for Mr

Parsons, its regular Norsewood correspondent. People like your style of writing, so why not come and work for us, the editor repeatedly asked. No, she always responded. Her loyalty to her elderly parents remained stronger than the lure of full-time employment.

Hannah's second home in Norsewood was barely 100 metres away – in Eric Street, the continuation of Coronation Street where they lived. The Salvation Army's old hall in Lower Norsewood had burnt down in 1915, and the next one had been built in Eric Street. Hannah was the church organist and accompanist at their concerts. She was a good elocutionist and her humorous monologues were very popular. She loved the music and the meetings, and so the Salvation Army and its activities played a major role in her life. And, of course, Albert was there.

Albert had been only 14 and newly employed as a bush worker, when an accident cost him his right leg. They had been playmates at school and now, as adults, they had rediscovered each other. It was joyfully understood that in their work for the Salvation Army, they would keep together and serve the Lord on good days as well as bad. Big heavy Albert, with his crutches, and petite little Hannah, with her warm smile, had reached a secret agreement.

The Lord provided plenty of work for them both. Temptations abounded on Saturday nights. It took considerable strength to bear witness to Jesus outside the Crown Hotel – not to mention inside – where the air was blue with one thing or another. They did not enter the theatre at the end of the street when the Saturday dances were held there. They both knew what dancing led to, Mother had warned her more than once. Still, it was different when silent films screened there and Uncle Julius played the accompaniment, that was sophisticated entertainment – untainted by sin.

The Mariboe house enjoyed a stream of visitors. The boys continued returning home each weekend while they operated the Makaretu Sawmill. However, it was another story when they moved to the King Country. They became proud owners of motorbikes, especially Daniel, who owned a particularly big and powerful bike. Now, was it a Norton or perhaps a B.S.A.? Whatever it was, it could be heard well before it arrived, and when he came to town, admiring little boys arrived too.

'Give us a ride, Dan?' And kind Dan would oblige.

Old Tike the dog seemed able to tell both the time of day and the day of week, and would wait for the boys at the brow of the hill.

Grandchildren regularly came and went. Who stayed the longest? Who knew their grandparents best? Was it Niel? Was it Alex? Desmond perhaps? No, it was Ella-Ruth, Eva's daughter, who lived with her grandparents at Hillside Farm as a small child. Eileen, Sarah's only daughter, was perhaps the closest. She would arrive on the first day of the school holidays and leave on the last, and shared many of Johanna's interests. Not so much the spinning and knitting, but certainly the sketching and painting.

Hannah appreciated Eileen's company as well, and the pair did a lot of walking around the district. Sometimes during their travels, they met cousin Jane Brenkley, daughter of Johanna's sister, Karoline. Jane also enjoyed outdoor sketching, and would typically be gathering native plants as specimens for botanical sketches. In time she would be recognised widely for what would become known as 'folk art'.

'Look after that girl,' Jane used to say of Eileen. 'She'll be an artist one day.'

Jane and Eileen enjoyed interesting talks on their shared hobby, and their methods and work habits were similar. They shared the same sense of urgency, with quick sketches made outside to capture the spirit. Then they would head back home, where, with crayons, charcoal or watercolours, they would recreate the object on paper.

Goodness me! How history repeats itself! Johanna had

halted her spinning wheel to watch Eileen more than once. It was like seeing Old Paso all over again. Clearly, she was blessed with his gifts, and like him, she worked with such speed. A few quick, bold black lines and there was a cottage, a tumbledown shed or a horse in full flight . . .

She could see Old Paso fifty years back and more. A worn, wrinkled hand stained by the charcoal kept in his pocket. A few sure lines, all at speed, and then there were the wild animals, a fox slinking away, a bear eating blueberries . . . Blueberries! She could still remember their taste in her mouth.

Johanna had watched this new generation of Paso artists as they worked just as rapidly, it seemed, with their watercolours. A quick wash with one colour, then onto the next, and the next. Then the paper would be hung and allowed to dry slowly. Did Old Paso know about watercolours? Where would he have got them? Her thoughts drifted back to Odalen. Would the blue have come from the blueberries? How well she remembered her sisters' blue lips in the summer.

There were forty people – all family – at the Diamond Wedding celebration. The largest – and the last – contingent had arrived from Mananui. This was Arthur, his wife Else Lilly, and their six children. Johanna and Christian sat together on the verandah most of the day. Christian's body now objected when he rose from chairs and moving about drew a similar reaction. There were no toasts proposed during the main meal and no formal speeches, but the conversation flowed. The children – the adult children that is – came up to thank their Mama and Papa for all they had done for them. Of course, they had to lean close to achieve this as Christian's hearing was no longer the best.

'We are proud of you!' Were those Martin's words that kept ringing in her ears for a long time afterwards? Or had they all said much the same?

'We know you struggled hard to bring us up . . . Gave us a happy and a good start . . . Left your mark, see forty of us here today . . . Feel it was all worth it . . .' The odd tear had been wiped away.

'Do you feel it was all worth it?' Christian's voice was hoarse today. Johanna could only squeeze his hand back in reply.

Carl August – Charlie – was the last to come up, and he had an unexpected request. Could he please come home to live? He had not tasted alcohol for many months and there were jobs around the Mariboe house that needed attention. He was quite a handyman. Could anyone have wished for a better present for his or her Diamond Wedding?

Carl August stayed for two weeks following the Diamond Wedding and proved he really was a good worker. Fences were repaired and the two sheds at the back were repainted. The guttering needed attending to, but that could wait until he returned permanently in a few weeks. He got on well with his parents, especially his father, and would sit with him for hours. Mostly they discussed sheep, although Johanna noticed it was Carl August who usually did the talking. He promised to bring back a silver-grey fleece for her spinning. That would be nice.

Hannah and Eva followed him back to Tokomaru Bay to collect his belongings as arranged. However, when they arrived they found he had entered Te Puia Hospital. He was already better, he assured them, so much so he said he would come down to Norsewood in a few days. So the two women spent the night in his surprisingly tidy little red-painted cottage at the sheep station. The station manager gave Charlie an excellent testimonial. A very versatile worker who could do fencing and painting, bake bread and take over as the station cook when necessary. On top of all that, he was also a good shearer and musterer. He regretted losing him. Well, yes, he drank a little – apparently – from time to time, but it never interfered with his work.

Hannah and Eva had been back two days when the telegram came. Charles A. Christiansen had passed away at Te Puia Hospital.

Johanna and Christian took his death hard. After a while, though, Johanna could see God's hand in it all. Carl August had been remorseful when he was home, and had wanted to start a new life. He wanted his parents' forgiveness – and he wanted God to forgive him as well. And God had forgiven him, as God forgives remorseful sinners. She would meet her oldest son when the day came – and that day may not be far away.

15 The circle closes

Norsewood – in the summer of 1997. Sigga and Johan Bonnevie visit me at Halford Court. This is where I am staying, only a stone's throw from the pioneer museum. We stroll through the small town centre and note the old houses being spruced up in anticipation of the historic jubilee. Even Ambassador Kjell-Martin Frederiksen and his wife will visit during this event, all the way from Canberra, Australia. It is 125 years since the first settlers came here.

'Except for the asphalt and the bridge over the highway, everything is like it was when I walked here fifty years ago,' says Johan. 'It is strange to see how everything is preserved. Everything except the Mariboe House. That's where I met old Johanna.'

The dilapidated Mariboe House is, to be sure, still standing where it always stood, although it is now almost hidden in the wilderness behind the Norsewood Pioneer Museum. If it could be restored, what a storytelling contribution to the museum! Some people are working to do just that, I have heard.

Johan has never forgotten the meeting with 92-year-old Johanna, who was reputed to be the last survivor from those who arrived aboard the *Høvding*. At least, she was the last survivor from those hundreds of people anyone in the district knew of.

'I was incredibly lucky, arriving in Norsewood as a back-packer just in time for the wedding of Johanna's daughter. How I treasure those memories!'

'And I ran barefoot through the forest picking blueberries.'

She lay in bed and warmly held the hands of the unexpected guest. In fact, she wouldn't let them go. A young man from Norway! He even had the name Johan, and had come all the way from Norway! He had come from the country she left seventy-four years ago, and had arrived in the midst of Hannah's wedding. God must have sent him. She smiled happily . . .

The tiny woman in the bed was too weak to attend the church where her daughter stood as bride. Still, she was participating anyway. Everyone had returned directly to her bedside following the ceremony, and had given her a running commentary – repeatedly – of the entire event. Her sons, daughters, children-in-law, grandchildren and great grandchildren, they all came into her room to see her, one after the other, and all had plenty of time to devote to her.

And then came one who spoke Norwegian!

Johanna closed her eyes. This meeting with a Norwegian, a young man who spoke the language of her childhood, triggered old memories. Once again, she was a little girl in the Skara forest.

So much had happened since then. Travel from the known to the unknown, the daily grind and the sacrifices, the accidents and the tragedies. The happy times in between, and at last, the change for the better. Now she was happy. Her children and grandchildren had achieved a good living in this unknown country they called Ny Seland.

Christian was called home to God two years after the Diamond Wedding. Apart from a few aches and pains and some hearing loss, he had been well until a few weeks before his death. His last fortnight was spent in Dannevirke Public Hospital, where he passed away on 16 March 1938.

March, always March, Johanna had thought. March had been the month of the big flood when he almost lost his life. March was when he was lost in the ranges, March of the big fire, and now . . . She missed him terribly. The empty cane chair on the verandah, his basket for the carded wool now empty, their bed so cold and empty. Yes, empty – that was how she felt. She cooked too much food and constantly laid an extra plate on the table. He remained part of her life, but as a shadow.

'The Salvation Army has lost a staunch supporter and a devoted member,' Major Lamond had said at the graveside. Johanna had dried her tears then. She was very proud of him. The many telegrams and bunches of flowers had shown her how much he had been appreciated. Perhaps, though, it was the telegram from Salvation Army Headquarters in Wellington she had appreciated most of all.

Increasingly she missed her mother tongue. They had spoken Norwegian when no one else was around. It was the language of the late evenings, of the night and the early morning. Small personal secrets, incidents from the past and words of intimacy were whispered in Norwegian. It provided a special bond between them. They had been making more use of it too, Johanna thought, as they were alone more often and the nights seemed longer.

Admittedly, there was a fair bit of Norwegian still spoken in Norsewood, but it was just social small talk. Pleasant enough, but with no real depth. Not the Norwegian she and Christian had shared.

Johanna missed her animals too. Animals had always surrounded her. Old Tike the dog, was long since dead, so too was dear Sybil. Friends had accepted her when Christian could no longer get hay for her, or rather when the pitchfork had become too difficult to handle. Would a cat be any company? A big warm fluffy cat to smooch around her ankles and sit on her lap. And she could even talk to her in Norwegian!

Well, yes, perhaps. Christian had not been in favour of cats. They scared birds and he wanted so much to attract bellbirds to his garden. He had always felt guilty about the bellbirds. Still, would he have been able to hear them if they were there? Perhaps they visited already, but he had been unable to see them.

A new war came and eventually went, having borrowed nine of Johanna's grandsons. The Lord be praised, all had returned more or less safely. Young Ralph, who was wounded, was left with a permanent limp, and spent a long period as a prisoner of war. Herbert's health, however, was irreparably damaged.

Johanna knew the Germans had invaded Norway this time. Had they been to Odalen and seen the wonders of Skara forest? Had they found Pasotorpet? She would never know that her secluded childhood home had been a place of refuge for Norwegian patriots en route to the safety of Sweden.

Johanna had maintained contact with her relatives back in Norway, and regularly corresponded with her younger cousin, Rangdi Henriksen, in Odalen. Rangdi's father was Uncle Arne – the baby who had been saved from the burning church at Grue in 1822.

Johanna had last seen Rangdi in the yard at Kuggerud Farm as they prepared to leave for Christiania. She well recalled the restless toddler secure within her mother's clinging arms. Rangdi also remembered the gathering – or perhaps it was just talk of the gathering.

When Johanna's health began declining in the 1940s, her hands became too shaky to write. It seemed the link would finally be broken. There was no longer anyone who could write letters in Norwegian on her behalf. And Rangdi did not understand a word of English. Hannah, not wanting to see her mother – or the family – lose this precious connection, began writing to Rangdi in English.

Rangdi took Hannah's letters to a local schoolteacher, who translated the first letters, then passed the task on to a young pupil, Hans Marius Trøseid. Hans Marius lived close to Rangdi's home and was distantly related to the Paso family. This three-way correspondence would continue until Rangdi's death in the early 1950s.

It is noteworthy that the remaining parts of this triangle resumed unexpectedly in the early 1970s when Hannah tried to rediscover some Norwegian relatives.

Her letter to Rangdi's former address, seemingly from a stranger, eventually found its way to Hans Marius. Hannah had not known the name of the young man who had translated her letters so many years earlier – and at first he did not recognise her.

The connection finally made, though, the pair corresponded until Hannah's death. Hans Marius, local historian and schoolteacher, continued his involvement with the Paso family. He contributed research to both the Norwegian and English versions of this book.

Bless the spinning wheel! It gave feelings of comfort and quiet pleasure. It sang and hummed as she rocked ever so slowly and sang back to it. Hannah did the carding now. In fact, Hannah did everything. She encouraged people to visit and stay, entertained them and looked after them. She did the washing, made soap for the copper and, slowly, slowly, took over the cooking. She achieved this step so subtly Johanna hardly noticed the transition.

Together with Albert, Hannah was a tower of strength to the church. The two Salvation Army officers who conducted the Sunday service had their midday meal at the Mariboe house for how many years? It could have been decades.

Johanna's legs had become painful. Her knees were bad, but her hips were worse. Shopping was an ordeal, despite the shops being across the road. She had to rest on her bed several times a day. And from her bed she would summon Hannah – once more – for that familiar topic of conversation.

'Sit down, my dear. Here, where I can see you.'

'Yes Mother.' Hannah knew what was coming.

'How much longer will you keep poor Albert waiting?'

'We are engaged, Mother. He knows how I feel about him.'

'Yes, my dear, but I would so like to see you married – in time to have children.'

At this point, the conversation usually broke down. Albert – 'poor Albert' indeed – had been the postmaster at Ngamoko from 1916 until it closed on New Year's Eve 1931. Since then, he had devoted his life to his small farm at Ngamoko, the Salvation Army and, above all, to Hannah. He was very patient, understood her divided loyalties and did not rush her. Then there was also the important question as to who would look after Johanna when Hannah moved to Albert's farm following the marriage.

Still, this time Johanna had a reply. Both Eva and Sarah would stay at the Mariboe house while the newlyweds enjoyed their honeymoon in the South Island. Then after that – perhaps Johanna could move to the Ngamoko farm too?

Johanna's craftwork never stopped. It just tapered off as she increasingly spent her days in bed. There was not much spinning done towards the end. Her right leg was the most painful one. And even the spinning wheel seemed now to have only one song: 'it won't be long . . . it won't be long now'. She looked forward to being with Christian again. There were the others – Old Paso, Maren, her parents Johan and Randi, and her own brothers and sisters of course. Also her four children who had gone ahead. They were all waiting for her now. Of her entire extended family who had sailed on *Høvding*'s two voyages to New Zealand, only Johanna remained. If only she could see Hannah married . . .

She won her little battle. The date for the wedding had been set 'just to please Mother' Hannah wrote in her memoirs. It was to be the first Saturday in June 1947. So why then was it postponed to 9 July? Why then did poor Albert have to explain and write out new invitations? Was it fear of the unknown on Hannah's part? Or just playing for time? No, nothing of the sort. An unscheduled appendicitis attack had seen Hannah rushed to Dannevirke Hospital for an operation.

Johanna, who was now largely bedridden, had been up in the morning. She had seen the guests off as they left for church. Only Hannah and Albert, with his crutches, had travelled by car. Everyone else walked the short distance up the road to the Salvation Army Hall in the crisp, winter sunshine.

A tourist disembarked from the bus in Upper Norsewood that day. Was this the place where many Norwegians had settled so long ago? Would anyone be left who spoke the language?

He gazed at the quaint village in front of him. To his left was a forest in many shades of dark green. Above this was pale blue winter sky – there would be a frost tonight. There was something strangely familiar about this scene.

Big dusty pre-war American cars lined the street. Perhaps they had travelled a long way to look like that. A big garden to the right drew his eye. Many people milled about in there, people of all ages. The men, in their fifties or perhaps their sixties, seemed strangely similar. Solidly built, but not too tall, and all wearing black suits.

There was only one tall person to be seen. He was tall, very strong looking, and also in a dark suit. But oh, poor man, he was on crutches! Beside him was a petite woman who was radiant with smiles. She was wearing a pale blue outfit and holding a bouquet in her hands. They looked like a bridal couple, despite being past their youth. Would he dare enter the garden and wish them well?

Was the stranger really from Norway? Did he speak the language? Martin is the best of us at the language. He lived with Grandmother a lot.

'Martin, there is someone who would like to talk with you!'

But Martin could no longer converse in Norwegian beyond *Godag, Godag.*

Yes, he was from Oslo – that was Christiania – had been in the country some weeks, was going to return to Norway shortly – was called Johan . . .

Mother would be so pleased to see you – and to talk with you. She is the oldest person in Norsewood, and the last living person we know of who came out seventy-five years ago. A little weak now . . . mostly in bed.

How friendly they all were! The visitor felt at ease. They were all sawmillers, it appeared. Two came from Owhanga, now where was that? They wanted to include him in the wedding party, it seemed.

Martin led the way. Up the steps and across the verandah . . . Inside the house, to the right, was a bedroom. Its door was half open.

'Mother, we have a visitor for you. One who speaks your language.'

A bed to the left on the inside wall, a huge Bible on a small table, a wicker chair and a painting in shades of green and gold. Oh, and Martin Luther, of course, very stern looking. Johan took it all in, but it was the old lady who held his attention. So frail looking, so old, and she seemed so small under her patchwork quilt. He disregarded the chair, sat on the edge of the bed, took her hand – and they talked and talked and talked . . .

Really, it was Johanna who did most of the talking. Johan was such a good name. Her son had been Johan, her father was Johan, and there had been Johans in every generation at Pasotorpet. Did this Johan know where Odalen was? Did he know about the Skara forest and the blueberries?

The wedding guests came in from the garden in twos and threes, listened for a while then tiptoed out again. Johanna seemed elated. Perhaps she was talking about her childhood.

Indeed she was. Decades slipped away. She was back at Pasotorpet with the animals. The language seemed quaint to Johan, he had not heard her dialect before, but the pictures she painted were crystal-clear. It was July in the Skara forest once more, high summer. The trees with their red bark, the clouds, the distant blue hills, the long days, the warm smell of summer, and the big shiny blueberries. It was all so close, and for this brief period, the past was again the present.

'And I ran barefoot through the forest picking blueberries.'

Johanna Johansdatter 'Paso' Christiansen died peacefully at Ngamoko on 13 October 1948. She is buried at the Norsewood Cemetery beside her beloved Christian.